£4·95p

Small
Craft
Conversion

BY THE SAME AUTHOR

A Taste for Sailing, Adlard Coles Ltd, 1969
Small Boat Conversion, Rupert Hart-Davis, 1951
(Paperback: Bosun Books) 1963
A Ship Modeller's Logbook, Percival Marshall, 1950

Anatomy of Printing, Faber/Watson Guptill, USA, 1970
The Graphic Reproduction and Photography of Works of Art
(with Edwin Smith), Cowell/Praeger, USA, 1969
The Twentieth Century Book, Studio Vista/Reinhold, USA, 1967
Illustration: Aspects and Directions (with Bob Gill),
Studio Vista/Reinhold, USA, 1964
Typography: Basic Principles, Studio Vista/Reinhold, USA, 1963
Printed Ephemera, Faber/Dover, USA, 1962
A Handbook of Type and Illustration, Cowell/Faber, 1956
Graphic Design (with John Brinkley), Routledge & Kegan Paul, 1954

To the last of the individualists, the small craft converters

Acknowledgements

I would like to thank the many friends and strangers who have so generously helped me with information about their conversions, and particularly Hervey Benham for both practical advice and for his introductions to a number of his fishing-boat-owning friends. Of these I must thank Michael Frost for telling me the detailed story of the rebuilding of his wonderful old Maldon smack *Boadicea*, Donald Rainbird for information about the rebuilding of his Colchester smack *Mayflower*, Charles and Janet Harker for information about their Aldous smack *Iris* and also about their Baltic trader *Solvig*, Bryan Thomas for information and plans of his converted Brightlingsea smack *Shamrock*, Stephen Swann and his partners for information about their Leigh bawley *Bona*, Peter Bailey for lending me photographs and giving me information about his Norwegian fishing smack *Boan*, and Richard Riggs for similar help about his Norwegian dory conversion *Marka*.

I would also like to thank Richard Horncastle for information about his Tholen hengst *Elizabeth Josina*, H. J. van der Werff of Goes, S. Beveland, for drawings and photographs of his lifeboat cutter *Sonnevaert*, Sem Hartz of Haarlem for information about Dutch craft and José Braz of Sesimbra for help in obtaining plans and details of Portuguese fishing boats. My gratitude must also go to John David Rogers for his photographs and information about the conversion of his whaler to the fin-keel ketch *Petrel*, to Richard F. Day of Don Mills, Ontario for information and drawings of his whaler conversion, to Wilfrid Peake of Manningtree for information about his barge yacht. I would also like to thank Stan Smyth for details of his Debutante conversion and Arthur G. Taylor and Gerald Dennis, the Maldon sailmakers, for information about the sails of fishing smacks. I would like to record Kenneth Gibbs' help in my previous book, including much of the material about engine installation which is used here. I can never forget the late William Porter of Manningtree who taught me so much when we were converting my lifeboat ketch. I am particularly grateful to three naval architect friends, to Maurice Griffiths GM, for reading the manuscript and making many helpful suggestions, and to Jack Francis Jones and his partner Peter Brown who generously helped me in many ways.

Lastly my thanks to the Woodbridge boat builders Frank Knights Ltd and particularly to Frank Knights himself and to Philip Gouch and Bob Brewster for much practical help and information, and to Keith Cutmore of the same firm for drawings and many facts about motor fishing vessels and the installation of their engines and gear.

Contents

List of Drawings

List of Photographs

Introduction

Making something out of not very much has an everlasting appeal. The restoration of crumbling old cottages is the most obvious manifestation of this. The conversion, even the rebuilding, of old fishing boats or ships' lifeboats into craft that go to sea or travel the inland waterways is another. There is more to it than trying to get something for nothing. There is the very real pleasure of actually planning and carrying out the work of converting, shall we say, a ship's lifeboat into a useful little ship. The restoration of an old fishing smack into something like its original condition has added pleasurable factors of research and rescue of types of craft that might be lost for ever, but the latter work demands considerable knowledge of the shipwright's craft.

Most conversion work needs at least the skills of the average handyman and infinite patience. Unlike house building, there are very few straight lines in a boat and a lot of time can be spent 'offering up' work, before it can finally be fitted. Hulls traditionally built of wood are still available, but some consideration ought to be given to glassfibre and steel hulls.

My first conversion was of a 26 ft ship's lifeboat into a sailing ketch. In this conversion my efforts were mainly confined to the design for the conversion and to acting as an unskilled labourer. The fact that I knew nothing —absolutely nothing—about boat work and the difference between common or garden carpentry and the job of the shipwright, led me to ask a thousand elementary questions that someone more experienced than I would have taken for granted. The notebooks that I kept at that time were the foundations of this book and its predecessor.*

Since those happy days when we converted our 26 ft lifeboat into the ketch *Grace Darling*, much has happened in the world of yachting. There has been a mushroom growth in the sport and every year thousands more boats are launched. To meet this new market, series production-line methods have been established, with every boat looking exactly like its predecessor. Few people can now afford to have one-off yachts built. The boat converter and the boat restorer stand almost alone as the real individualists. No two conversions, even from the same basic hull, ever need look the same. Materials cost more than they used to, but one's own labour is still one's own—so if there was a case for conversion twenty years ago, there is an even stronger case today.

Before one starts on a conversion or a restoration, or even begins to look for a hull, one should decide for what use the boat is intended. Is it to be used for canal or river work on quiet inland waters, is it to sail estuaries, or is it to be used for deep-sea work? The differences in design, construction and cost are considerable for each of these different types.

Small craft suitable for conversion

Shipping companies and navies renew their lifeboats and other small craft regularly, so superannuated boats come onto the market in a steady trickle. In Great Britain, the Director of Navy Contracts, from the Admiralty, Bath, periodically issues lists of available craft. The Board of Trade advertises larger craft for sail. Otherwise recognized dealers in surplus craft advertise in the yachting press.

* Small Boat Conversion, John Lewis. Rupert Hart-Davis, London, 1951

Hulls can vary from a few pounds or dollars to many thousands of pounds and can include not only ships' lifeboats (wood, steel and glassfibre) but large motor fishing vessels, harbour craft, whalers, dinghies and pontoons.

Ships' lifeboats, which in some ways offer most scope for conversion, are designed with one purpose in mind: to save the shipwrecked. To do this they must be seaworthy craft. Apart from keeping afloat and dry, they should also be able to reach the nearest land or shipping lane down wind. For seaworthiness they are beamy, light-displacement craft, with sharp pointed sterns, presenting the least resistance to following seas. They carry one or two dipping lugs, a handy enough rig under which they can blow along. They do not go well to windward. If your conversion is to be a sailing boat, that is, to cruise in estuaries and rivers or along the coast, it must be able to go to windward, so your lifeboat has to be given a more weatherly rig and a deeper keel, to give her more lateral resistance. Alternatively, you may keep her rig and keel unaltered and merely fit a powerful engine, so making her a motor-sailer.

All sailing vessels are a compromise. Factors such as draught, lines, accommodation and sail plan all affect a boat's performance, and what you gain by one factor may be at the expense of others. For instance in the matter of rig: a tall bermudan sloop rig, given a suitable hull, is the most efficient sail plan for getting to windward; a gaff ketch is one of the least effective for this purpose; yet the ketch with its smaller, more easily handled sails and lower masts is a better counterpart for a lifeboat's unweatherly hull.

In any conversion, the first thing to decide is for what purpose the boat is to be used; the second, how much time and money you want to spend on her; the third, whether you have had enough woodworking experience to warrant your undertaking a major conversion, or whether you had better content yourself with something fairly simple. In considering the various types of hulls available, let us start with ships' lifeboats.

Ships' lifeboats

Ranging from 18 ft to 30 ft long, ships' lifeboats, if in good condition, can make useful sailing cruisers. To give the 18-footers performance to windward the simplest method is to fit leeboards. With a gunter or gaff sloop rig and a low cabin they will make quite roomy little cruisers. A small inboard motor is well worth considering, for they will never be great performers to windward.

For this conversion, or for anything more ambitious with larger craft, you will have to gut the boat. This means stripping out all lockers and lifting out the keelson. Leave in the thwarts (seats) until the deck beams are in place, or the boat will go out of shape. For larger lifeboats (24–30 ft) some windward ability can be obtained by fitting either a false keel or bilge keels. In either case the hull will need considerable strengthening by means of floors (heavy cross members) and stringers (fore-and-aft members). Once deck beams and/or bulkheads have been fitted, the thwarts can be removed.

Whalers

British Naval whalers are either 25 or 27 ft long, with a narrow beam of only 6 ft and a draught of 1 ft 8 in. or 3 ft 9 in. with the centreboard down. In their normal use they are yawl rigged with unstayed masts. They get along quite well under this rig, but it is possible to convert them into very lively and fast little sailing cruisers. Their inherent limitation is their lack of beam and, when converted, their inevitable lack of headroom. They do, however, provide the most interesting *sailing* craft of any small conversion.

Open beach boats

There is an infinite variety of open boats used for inshore fishing. In Britain alone there are, for example, the solid little toshers of Mevagissey in Cornwall, the apple-cheeked beach boats of Brighton and Hastings, the transom-sterned Aldeburgh boats, the pointed-sterned Sheringham boats, the cobles of Yorkshire, and so on. All these boats will stand some degree of conversion, either back to sail, as an act of restoration, for they are all powered nowadays, or, with the addition of modest cabin trunks and decking, into little cruisers. It is even possible to convert a bridging pontoon into a little barge suitable for sailing in protected waters.

Pontoons

Pontoons, which are usually about 20 by 6 ft, come onto the market at different times. They can make very roomy little river boats which a 4 h.p. outboard will push along nicely. You can build on a cabin with about 5 ft headroom which need not be too unsightly if properly designed. I have even seen a pontoon that has been converted into a very small barge-yacht. This was done by turning her back to front, adding a deadwood to the swimhead to make the stern, taking out the transom and drawing the two sides together to make a pointed stem. This conversion, though economical in material, took quite a long time. The forward part was decked in and a small cuddy was built aft of the mast. A gaff sloop rig and a pair of substantial lee-boards completed the job. She sailed quite well, was handy, and her performance to windward in fairly smooth waters was surprisingly good.

Anyone interested in conversions, and particularly in converting a ships' lifeboat, should read *The Falcon on the Baltic* by Edward Frederick Knight. This is the tale of an old P & O lifeboat bought at Hammersmith in the summer of 1886 for £20, and of her cruise from Hammersmith to the Manningtree River, where some sixty years later we converted our lifeboat (Chapter 5). Knight sailed from Manningtree over the North Sea to Holland and the Baltic. He expressed something of the philosophy of the conversion mania when he wrote:

> When I bought the lifeboat, her sides were tarred, an act of atrocious vandalism, for her skin (which was double-diagonally planked) was of the cleanest and most beautifully-grained teak; so now all the tar was burnt off, she was scraped and her natural loveliness revealed. When she had been sandpapered and varnished she looked a very different sort of craft from of old. No picture-dealer who discovers some rare old master under a smoky daub ever effected so marvellous a transformation as did we with this once black, heavy-looking old tub.

One word of warning: conversion, no matter how well it is done, is not a money-making proposition. But it can provide you, for a very small *initial* outlay, with a boat that you will be fond of, that will do all you should ask of her, and sometimes more than her more yacht-like sisters. My advice would be to get the boat sailing as soon as you can, adding to cabin comforts and other refinements each winter. Apart from everything else, converting a lifeboat, for instance, into a sailing cruiser is worth while for what you will learn in the process about boats and the way they are built.

ONE

Methods of working, surveys, tools and materials

When building any boat of wood and by traditional methods, keel blocks and a keelboard have to be set up. The keelboard for a 26 ft lifeboat would be a 9 in. by 3 in. plank set up on its edge on top of the blocks, at about 30 in. from the ground, so that the hull can be got at from below. The same method should be used for a conversion, allowing some rake by chocking the front so that the waterline will be exactly level. Likewise the boat must be chocked on either side so that transversely her thwarts are also level. In building a boat, supports from the rafters of the building shed will keep it in position. When conversions have to be done in the open air this is not possible, so temporary 'legs' may have to be bolted to the topsides. In case of large craft, such as fishing smacks or MFVs, conversion work may well have to be done when the craft is afloat or at least in a mud berth. If the latter is the case, it is worth going to some trouble to get the boat on an even keel.

If it is possible for the converter to get some practical help from a ship-wright, he can learn more in a few hours than he can learn from the study of any book. The basic difference between the joinery on a boat and house carpentry is that in house building the stresses are only those imposed by gravity, whereas in a boat at sea there are stresses in every direction. It may be quite enough to spike a rafter to a sill in house building, but if one tried such methods in boatbuilding, he would be in trouble. In the 1914–18 war there was such a shortage of shipping that a firm of house builders in Halifax, Nova Scotia, was given the job of building some wooden cargo ships. The first one they built and launched in record time. As they started to load her up with cargo of coal, strange creaks and groans came out of the hull. These reached such alarming proportions that they only put about a quarter of her

1 14 ft Medway sailing punt used for cruising, with clothes and gear stowed in tins and watertight boxes alongside centreboard case

2 20 ft Sheringham crab boat with foredeck and cabin, used for both cruising and fishing

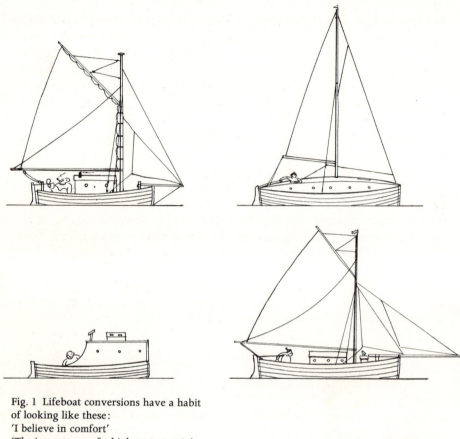

Fig. 1 Lifeboat conversions have a habit
of looking like these:
'I believe in comfort'
'The importance of a high aspect ratio'
'She's a homey little boat'
'There's nothing like a gaff cutter'

capacity in her. The water was glassy smooth as she left the quay for her
maiden voyage across the harbour. She had not gone more than 500 yards
when she was seen to be down by the stern. As the captain gave orders to
abandon ship, she slowly disintegrated. Her bottom had fallen out.

In house building, wire nails may be enough. In boat building, you use
copper nails and rivets or heavy screws for the planking and heavy bolts
for the backbone of the keel, stern and stemposts and deadwood. This book
is NOT a treatise on boat building. The difficulties, for instance, of shaping
the curved edge of the planks that come near the turn of the bilge are something that most boat converters will not have to worry about. If planks have

to be replaced, the best thing to do is to take out the damaged plank and scribe the replacement to its exact pattern. In boat building one never uses butt joints: beams are always dovetailed or morticed and bolted, and planks are scarphed.

In building boats, as well as the problems of stresses and strains, there is the all-important matter of keeping the water out, and not only from coming through the hull, but also through the decks, cabin trunk, etc. This is both for safety and comfort and also against the possible damages of rot in a wooden boat, or corrosion in a metal one. Here glassfibre scores. Places where rainwater can lodge are sure points for rot—a major worry in boat work. Rot in wood is caused by a fungus; construction methods and the proper choice of timber will help to eliminate this. Corrosion likewise is largely a matter of the proper choice of metals and the elimination of electrolysis or galvanic action. Any would-be boat converter must have some basic knowledge of what troubles to look out for, before buying a boat.

Most open boats, such as lifeboats and whalers, are unlikely to be suffering from extensive rot, particularly dry rot which flourishes only in conditions of little ventilation. In open boats possible danger points for rot are the gunwales. Check to see that there is no rot beneath the covering board. Also, if hulls have been out of water for some time, look at them from either end to make sure there has been no distortion or twist in their shape. Examine their fastenings. If they are iron fastened, see if the nails are rusty or loose; if copper nailed and riveted see if the rooves are hard up against the timbers. Refastening a nail-sick vessel is hardly worth considering though it is not too difficult to tighten up the copper rooves. Look at the hood ends (the ends of the planks at the stem or sternpost or transom). These will be fastened by screws and refastening them is not a difficult job. If brass has been used for the fastenings, they will almost certainly need replacing. In the case of surveying a decked craft such as an old fishing boat, the survey is much more complicated and here one is very likely to come up against rot in some form or other. (This is dealt with in detail later in the book in the chapter on converting fishing smacks.)

Steel lifeboats
To assess the condition of a steel lifeboat is not difficult and steel hulls certainly provide a satisfactory base for conversion and usually result in a leakproof boat. If the plates, usually $\frac{1}{8}$ in. or 3 mm thick, show an undue waviness it may be that they have rusted away too much. If this is so, I

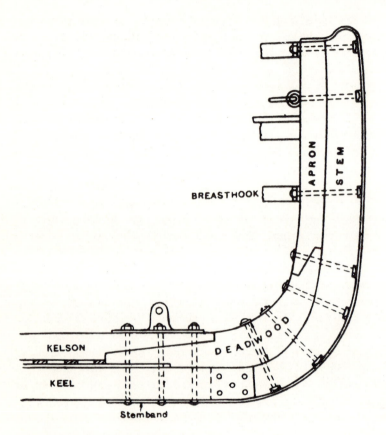

Fig. 2 The construction of the stem in a
wooden lifeboat

would condemn the boat out of hand. A good hard poke with a bradawl or
spike should give an indication of this. In the case of other steel-built craft,
a more thorough survey may well be justified. Danger points are between
wind and water, along the waterline and anywhere where rainwater may
have lodged. The way to check plates is, with the owner's permission, to
drill one or two holes through what appear to be sound plates and measure
the thickness. Plug these test holes with rivets, then drill anywhere that
looks suspect and check the thickness against that of sound plates. If there
is a material difference, condemn plates. If there are only a limited number,

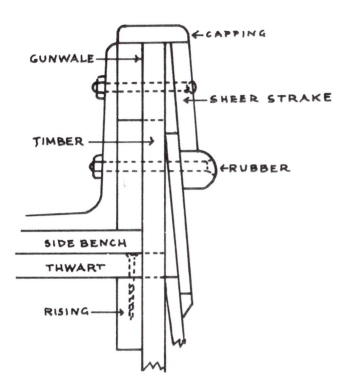

Fig. 3 The construction of the gunwale
in a wooden lifeboat

these can be cut out and new ones welded in position. Plates round bow and
stern are more difficult as they may have to be shaped. If these have to be
replaced, this may be an added reason for rejecting the boat. If, through
electrolysis, just one or two plates are badly worn away these again could be
replaced. The essential factor in undertaking the conversion of a steel hull
is familiarity with welding and working in metal, even if all the super-
structure, cabin tops, decks, etc. are to be in wood. These and suitable bulkheads have to be fastened to the steel hull. Lugs will have to be welded to the
hull, or to the ribs, to provide points of attachment. If you have no experi-

ence in this kind of work, it would be a folly to start without a previous course of instruction in welding, oxy-acetylene cutting and even panel-beating.

Glassfibre lifeboats
Some shipping lines are now using glassfibre for their lifeboats, but recently I heard of at least one line that has reverted to traditionally built wooden boats. Glassfibre lifeboats, if they come on the market, may well be there because they are of poor quality. When you are examining one, if the moulding shows a multitude of hairline cracks, or other evidence of crazing, this could be an indication of poor quality production. However, if the boat has not suffered any distortion and has no bad cracks or evidence of dela-mination she may be quite a good proposition. When she is converted she will certainly need painting, so hairline cracks, scratches or discolouration will not matter. Glassfibre boats like every other kind of craft need mainten-ance. For conversion work they need kid gloves as well. It is a material that imposes its own techniques.

Tools, fastenings, ballast, ironwork, rigging, timber, order of work

Shipwrights' tools
Adzes, axes and caulking mallets, ball-peen hammers and scrapers may not often come the way of the domestic carpenter. Apart from the ball-tipped hammer, used for heading soft copper nails over rooves (rivets), the con-verter working in wood can almost manage with a good kit of joiners' tools. The main thing is that saws and chisels should be kept sharp. It is no econ-omy using cheap tools. If you are inexperienced, go and take some lessons at your local technical college. Of the best books on the subject listed here, the last one is now (1972) out of print:

BOAT CARPENTRY by Hervey Garrett Smith. D. Van Nostrand, New Jersey
BOAT BUILDING by Howard I. Chapelle. Allen & Unwin, London, 1966
COMPLETE AMATEUR BOAT BUILDING by Michael Verney. John Murray, London
EVERY MAN HIS OWN SHIPWRIGHT by James I. Bell. Chantry Publications, London

It is certainly not necessary to equip yourself with a full range of ship-wrights' tools in order to convert a lifeboat. But there are one or two things that the household carpenter might not have. Clamps (also called cramps),

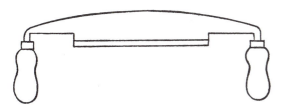

Fig. 4 Drawknife. This is used with the
bevelled side upwards

for instance, are essential; for the singlehanded workman they become so
many extra pairs of hands. Clamps are usually of wrought iron and are of
various sizes. I would suggest two pairs of 24 in. sash clamps, six pairs of
6 in. G-clamps, and two pairs of 3 in. G-clamps. (A pair of clamps is one
complete clamp—not two.)

You will need a coarse ripsaw with about 6 teeth to the inch, a fairly fine
panel saw, 10 to 12 teeth to the inch, a small tenon saw and a keyhole saw.
You will also need a Stanley $2\frac{1}{4}$ in. smoother, a $2\frac{5}{8}$ in. jackplane, and a $1\frac{3}{8}$ in.
block plane, and a baby Record plane which can fit into the palm of one hand
is most useful for all sorts of small jobs. A rabbet plane is also essential.

You will need: chisels for mortising, say $1\frac{1}{2}$ in. firmer, 1 in. bevelled,
$\frac{3}{4}$ in. paring, $\frac{1}{2}$ in. mortise, $\frac{1}{4}$ in. bevelled, and a mallet; a spokeshave and a
drawknife for cleaning spars (a drawknife is a two-handled tool (Fig. 4)
used bevelled side upwards); a $1-1\frac{1}{2}$ lb. claw-headed hammer, and an 8 oz.
one with a rounded head for clenching rooves; a bradawl, a gimlet, a brace,
and a set of bits, including long auger bits for drilling the false keel; pliers
and pincers, a large and a small screwdriver, a 3 ft rule, a set-square and a
spirit level, a plum-bob and line, and a chalk line. Power-driven tools are of
course invaluable.

Finally you will need something to work on. For our lifeboat conversion
we used a heavy 3 in. plank, 12 in. wide and 10 ft long, as our bench.
During the winter it was laid across the thwarts inside the boat, and in fine
weather on trestles on the marsh alongside. On your bench you will need a
vice of ample size; it should be at least 8 in. across.

Fastenings

The usual fastenings are copper nails and rooves, iron spikes which may or
may not be clenched, ring-barbed nails, or flat-point galvanised iron (or

steel) nails. Copper nails, properly rooved, are the best fastenings for out-side planks. Never use iron spikes, galvanised or not, with mahogany, because they react on the wood and set up rot.

Drill a hole and countersink it before driving the nail through. A copper nail will bend and buckle even in soft wood unless a hole is drilled first, but be sure it is a tight driving fit. The diameter of the hole should equal the thickness of the square nail. A copper washer, or roove, has to be fitted over the nail on the inside of the plank. Drive the roove up against the wood and snip off the point of the nail, leaving about $\frac{1}{8}$ in. projecting. Now this is where you must have help, for someone must hold a heavy weight against the head of the nail when you clench the soft copper over the roove. We used an old 7 lb. flatiron. While one person holds this in position the other hammers down the projecting part of the nail onto the roove with a round-headed hammer. Give three or four blows with the round end and finish off with the flat part. When using iron flat-points, drill as for other fastenings and drive the nail in so that the flat-point is across the grain of the timber or frame.

Use naval bronze or brass screws for everything else but the keel, stem and sternpost assembly, which should be bolted. Screws should be three times as long as the thickness of the plank to be fastened. They are sold by length and gauge.

For fastening tongue-and-groove planking to the deck you can use cut spikes or screws. Cut spikes hold better than nails. Galvanised iron spikes can be driven into soft wood planks without drilling. They are stronger than copper but the galvanising wears off in time and rust marks begin to appear.

To clench a nail, drive it through from the outside, snip off all but about $\frac{3}{8}$ in., turn $\frac{1}{4}$ in. of the end towards the timber and bang this projecting piece over, burying it in the wood at an angle of about $30°$ to the line of the grain. For $\frac{3}{4}$ in. or 1 in. planking use Nos. 11 or 12 copper nails and $\frac{3}{8}$ in. rooves. You can buy boat fastenings from ship and yacht chandlers.

Ironwork

Ship chandlers stock such ironwork as spider bands, gudgeons and pintles, cranse irons and shroud plates, but more often than not your fittings will have to be specially made. Make careful drawings of what you need, and then go and see your nearest blacksmith or engineering workshop and ask them to give you a price for making and galvanising.

3 *Grace Darling*, 26 ft lifeboat ketch:
the author's conversion afloat in
Hamford Water

Ballast

Most converted sailing cruisers will need some ballast. The 26 ft lifeboat
ketch needed about 900 lbs. This I had cast at the local ironworks in 60 lb.
slabs. These proved rather heavy to handle and I would recommend pieces
of about 30 lb. One sq. ft of $\frac{1}{2}$ in. iron plate weighs 20 lbs. One cu. ft of cast
iron weighs between 440 and 450 lbs., 1 cu. ft of lead weighs 720 lbs. In
other words, the ratio of weight of lead to iron is approximately 11:7.

When stowing your ballast, take great care that none of it rests on the
planks. If it is in small pieces, lay battens over the timbers, nail them into
position and then rest the ballast on them. If you think there is any danger
of the ballast sliding about or coming adrift, cover it with galvanised chicken
wire which can then be nailed into position against the hog, floors, and
timbers.

Wire rigging

In large craft the standing rigging, such as shrouds and stays, should be of
$\frac{7}{8}$ in. circumference plough steel wire. This has a wire heart, and is not very

flexible. For a 26 ft lifeboat or a 27 ft whaler use $\frac{7}{8}$ in. flexible steel wire with a hemp heart. Dress the wire with linseed oil diluted with 1 part of petrol to 4 of oil, or you may use hot boiled linseed oil or lanoline. Always use chain for your bobstay as the constant immersion will rust through any steel bar or wire rigging (see notes on rigging in Chapter 2).

Blocks

The cheapest blocks are made of elm, but are without strops, which you will have to fit yourself. Blocks fitted with internal strops are good but expensive. Stropping is quite simple. For lightness, Tufnol and similar blocks are widely used. They cost much more than simple unstropped elm or ash blocks.

Timber

The timber is a most important item in a conversion. For the 26 ft lifeboat ketch we used English oak for all structural framework: floors, bulkhead frames, cabin trunk uprights and beams, king plank and deck beams. We also used it for the keel, but here elm would have been just as good. For bulwark rails, deck planks and cabin top planks we used British Columbian pine. This is, however, a tricky wood, very liable to rot if both sides are sealed with paint or varnish. It is better to use white wood (or deal), or such African mahoganies as makore or sapele. When wide planks are needed, iroko is an excellent and knot-free wood. For all the framing of lockers, cupboards, etc. and for floorboard supports we used white wood or deal, for they only had to support locker doors and to hold fastenings.

OAK. Seasoned autumn-cut English oak is one of the best woods for all framing, including beams and floors.

LARCH. Our 26 ft lifeboat was planked with larch on oak timbers, as lifeboats normally are. Larch makes good planking, lasts well and is reasonably tough. In a sixty-year-old lifeboat at Manningtree, from the old S.S. *Columbia,* the larch planks were still sound though the oak timbers and copper fastenings have had to be replaced.

ENGLISH ELM. Elm should not be seasoned. It should be felled in winter and used as soon afterwards as possible. Elm is very durable under salt water, but it rots quickly in fresh. If you make your keel of English elm, scrub it clean and tar it before laying up for the winter. Do not use English elm for your floors as it will rot very quickly there, nor for the false keel, if your boat is to lie in a mud berth and dry out between tides.

PITCH PINE. This is a highly resinous, tough wood, very suitable for planking, particularly below the water. It is highly resistant to rot and excellent for carlings and stringers. Its only disadvantage is that it does tend to 'weep' resin and the seams between pitch pine planks will always show.

BRITISH COLUMBIAN PINE. This needs picking with care and is not as good as pitch pine. Never use it for a boat intended for fresh-water sailing, or in a badly ventilated position. It can rot within a year. If one side is left unpainted, and open to the air, it will last quite well.

TEAK. Teak is the finest of all woods for planking. It will stand sun or sea without warping or shrinking, and is extremely hard and durable—but it is very expensive and it is heavy. In thin boards it splits easily and must always be drilled for fastenings.

GREENHEART. This is a very hard timber which is so tough that nails cannot be driven into it. It is used for baulks and piles. It can also be used for rudders, keels and bottom planking, for it is teredo-resistant, but it will not bend easily. It is best cut when green, for a seasoned log will blunt any saw blade almost instantly. Its main use on boats is for fairleads, belaying pins or for any place where there is liable to be chafe. It was used in Revenue cutters for the planking on their foredecks, to take the wear of the anchor chains. Greenheart is very heavy, much heavier than either teak or oak. Its dust and splinters are poisonous, so it is not a pleasant wood to work. A splinter can cause a nasty sore.

IROKO. This is a tough, wide-planked, knot-free hardwood, which, when freshly sawn, is a banana colour. After exposure to sunlight it darkens to a grey-brown. It is excellent for cabin sides or anywhere where brightwork is to appear. It is also very useful for topside planking.

SPRUCE. Spruce is tough and wonderfully light; it is ideal for dinghies and prams that have to be lifted inboard. It is far the best wood for spars. For this purpose it should be brought in undressed poles, that is, with the bark still on the wood. These poles should be picked for their straightness, resilience and even spacing of knots. When stripped with a drawknife they will soon dry and become much lighter. As they dry, shakes will appear; these are longitudinal cracks in the spar, and are of no consequence. But when the spar is completed, these cracks should be filled with a *soft* stopping. To make the stopping, dissolve $\frac{1}{2}$ lb. resin in $\frac{1}{2}$ pint of hot linseed oil, and then dissolve a further $\frac{1}{4}$ lb. beeswax while the oil is still hot. Take the pan off the stove and add 3 oz. turpentine. Stir the mixture and allow it to cool. It sets into a soft substance which can be worked into the cracks as if it were putty. *Never* use ordinary putty that sets hard. Soft stoppings can be bought from ship chandlers already made up.

CANADIAN ROCK ELM. This is a good hard wood, suitable for keels, floors and timbers. It is very durable under water. If you use it for your rail, make sure to cover it at once with several good coats of varnish, or it will open up and small cracks will appear. It holds fastenings well but, when used for timbers, it can break at the turn of the bilge.

MAHOGANY. Only certain West African mahoganies are suitable for planking, either for interior or exterior work. They are not usually fully seasoned, so watch out for warping and shrinkage. The best mahogany for yacht building comes from Honduras. Do not use iron fastenings with mahogany, for iron will soon rot the wood.

The most suitable West African mahoganies are makore (it is the best of all, except that sawing it gives some people hay fever), *Khaya grandifolia*, a dark heavy wood (44 lbs to the cubic foot), *Khaya Ivorensis*, sapele and *Khaya anthotheca*. The last is subject to 'thunder shakes' or compression flaws across the grain, which are very hard to detect until the board is planed up. A 1 in. by 18 in. board will break under its own weight at one of these shakes, and they are sometimes only a few inches apart.

MARINE PLYWOOD. The obvious appeal to the amateur builder of plywood (so simple to work; such nice large sheets!) should not blind him to its defects. For interior work, for bulkheads, etc., it is usually far easier to fit tongue-and-groove planks, for it is difficult to offer up large sheets of ply and to scribe the shape of the ship's topsides. For exterior work, particularly for decking, it has an obvious use, but, even here, all is not easy. I may have been unlucky, but in two boats that I have had since I converted my 26 ft lifeboat, I have had trouble with plywood decks. In the first, after five years I had extensive rot and delamination. In the second, before she even left the builder's yard the surface of the painted ply decks was crazing, with a pattern of a million little hairline cracks. These freshly painted decks had to be sanded down, and then sealed with a patent sealer before they were repainted. Though marine ply may be manufactured to certain recognised trade standards (in Britain BS 1088), those standards cover only the gluing and not the wood itself, which is a rotary-cut veneer. The essential thing to do before painting is to seal both surfaces and edges with a patent sealer, or a phenolic resin waterproof glue or paint.

Taking off lines

This is not a difficult thing to do and it means that you have a proper basis on which to draw your conversion plans, or even to make a model and so

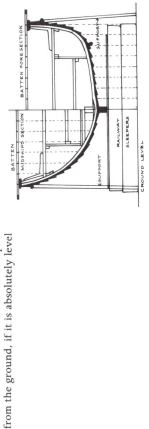

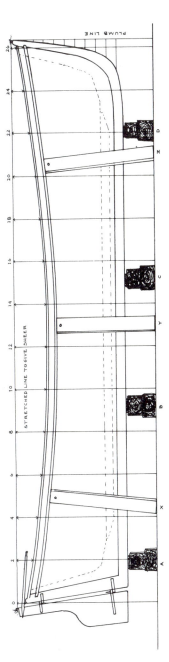

Fig. 5 Method of working and taking off lines. The hull is chocked up so that the intended waterline is level. With a line stretched fore and aft and with plumb lines the actual lines of the boat are transferred to paper. A, B, C and D are railway sleepers; X, Y and Z are supports bolted through the topsides.

The numbers on the stretched line are stations at 2 ft intervals, from which the sheer can be determined. Midships and fore sections: the shape can be determined either by measuring down from the batten inside the hull, or up from the ground, if it is absolutely level plan your conversion in three dimensions. If you have time and patience this is not a bad idea, because what looks all right on a plan may not look at all right when built. Such a model could be made of balsa wood, which is easy to work.

The procedure for taking off lines of an open boat, such as a lifeboat, is as follows: draw out rough sections in a large notebook, allowing one page per section. You can then mark in your figures on these rough diagrams. Get the boat on an even keel and level her up athwartships. Strip out all lockers, floorboards, etc. and then stretch a line from the top of the stem to the top of the sternpost; this should be a piece of Terylene or well stretched hambro line. You will need a spirit level, a long measuring tape, a foot rule and a 10 ft pole or batten marked in feet and inches, or in metric divisions. You will also need two people to help you do the job (two to measure, one to write it all down).

The sheer profile
1 Measure the fore and aft length along the stretched line.
2 Then at intervals of say 2 ft place the pole across the gunwales and take measurements from the stretched fore and aft line vertically downwards to the underside of the pole and from the underside of the pole to the top of the keel.
3 Drop a plumb line (i.e. a string with a weight on the end of it) from the top of the stem and sternposts (or centre of top of transom) and measure the height from ground; also at 12 in. intervals measure the horizontal distance from plumb lines to stem and stern. This will give the rake.

Transverse sections
1 Take vertical measurements from the pole at 6 in. intervals from the centreline to the gunwale at each 2 ft station. This will give you your sections and the inside dimensions of the boat.
2 To get the outside shape, add the thickness of the planking and measure the depth and the width of the keel. It may simplify things to coincide some of your stations with the thwarts.

Fishing smacks, etc.
It is not much more difficult to take off the lines from a decked boat. If the vessel can be chocked up on shore so that her waterline is level, the procedure differs only in that one arrives at the sheer and underwater profile by taking vertical measurements from the gunwale to the waterline and

from the keel to the waterline. The deck plan can be arrived at easily enough by taking measurements at right angles from the centreline (fore and aft) at specified stations, i.e. at 2 ft intervals.

To work out the sections, suspend the plumb line from the gunwale at the section stations. Then measure at one foot intervals down the line the distance horizontally from the plumb line to the side of the boat. These horizontal measurements will give you the section measurements. It is important to use a spirit level for these horizontal measurements and to make sure that the measurements are taken at right angles to the centreline of the hull and not to the curve of the planking. Measuring the thickness of the planking will give you the boat's inside measurements. If the craft has a counter (like a Colchester smack or a Lancashire nobby) this will need very close stations to get any accuracy into your lines. When you have all this information in your notebook, you can then go home and sit down and draw the vessel's lines. You do not need to be a professional naval draughtsman to do this. With a clean sheet of white paper, an accurate ruler, one or two flexible battens and a set square you can start work. Use an HB pencil and keep it sharp. When you have drawn out the lines of the boat, take a piece of tracing paper and lay it over your plan and sheer lines. On this, mark in accurately the position of the main timbers and floors and then the proposed position of your deck beams and bulkheads, so arriving at a simple construction plan of your hull. Once that is done, you can lay another piece of tracing paper over the construction plan and draw in your cabin trunk, hatchways, cockpit etc., both on the sheer and the plan view. You can thus make any number of alterations without spoiling your original construction plan of the hull. This tracing will show the major alterations and additions. Details of cabin fittings and so on can be on another sheet and your sail plan on yet another.

About the cabin fittings, there are one or two things to bear in mind. Particularly some essential dimensions. Over thirty years ago, Howard I. Chapelle in his book *Yacht Designing and Planning* gave these useful dimensions:

Berths should not be less than 6 ft 2 in. long and 21 in. wide. Pipe berths should be 6 ft 2 in. by 2 ft 6 in. if not shaped to the hull. All seats should be at least 16 in. wide and 12 in. above the floor, but the height may be decreased if the width is increased. You will need 3 ft 6 in. headroom over seats. There should be a minimum of 15 in. between the top of any cooking stove and the deck above. Clothes lockers should be 16 in. in width and 40 in. in height. Sinks if built in should not be less than 10

4 26 ft lifeboat ketch: fitting the sails

in. by 12 in. The minimum floor space for a WC is 16 in. by 18 in. If your side decks have to be less than 12 in. wide, carry the cabin top to the side of the ship.*

People do not change shape much in thirty years, so these dimensions are still valid. There is a great temptation to try and squeeze far too much into any yacht. If your lifeboat conversion is to be a sailing boat and is less than 24 ft overall you cannot have standing headroom throughout, so keep the cabin height down to sitting headroom, which is about 4 ft 8 in. You may be able to get bare standing headroom under the main hatch or doghouse. When you have completed your plans and are satisfied with them, you can measure up for your timber and go and see your timber merchant. As soon as the plans have been drawn and the timber and fastenings bought, the

* *Yacht Designing and Planning,* Howard I. Chapelle, Norton, New York, 1936

5 26 ft lifeboat ketch on the saltings:
fife rail and bitts. Bill Porter, who did
most of the work on the conversion

tools assembled and the boat in position, it is time to plan the order of work. This is really very important, as it makes the work much easier, and prevents your wasting your efforts by having to undo work to get at places which have become inaccessible.

The order of work in converting a ship's lifeboat into a sailing auxiliary

1 Chock the boat up into position—so that what will be the new load waterline (LWL) is horizontal.
2 Strip out all gear, lockers, thwarts (except for two holding the boat together), ring-bolts, etc.
3 Clean out very thoroughly with a hose and a wire brush.
4 If in the open, fix up tarpaulin awnings to give protection from the weather.
5 If there is to be a false keel, draw out keelbolts and lift out rider keelson.
6 If false sternpost or raised stemposts are to be fitted, do so at this stage.
7 Clean out and prepare the inside for painting. If paintwork is bad, burn it off; otherwise brush it down with a wire brush. Paint. If on bare wood, one coat of thin red lead priming, two undercoats of white lead and one top coat of hard gloss. Each coat following the previous one as soon as it is dry. The bilges (i.e. below the bottom stringers) can be either red-leaded or varnished with a half-and-half mixture of tar and turpentine. At this stage it is probably advisable to order the ironwork, which includes the gudgeons and pintles for the rudder, goose neck and gaff jaw, mast bands, etc., chainplates, and keel bolts.
8 Make and fit floors and false keel; fasten floors and keel; make and fit mast steps. Cut and fit floorboards.
9 Fit chainplates.
10 Fit fore-and-aft shelf for supporting deck beams.
11 Make and fit cabin bulkhead uprights.
12 Cut slots in shelf for deck beams.
13 Make and fit deck beams and forward bulkhead beam with its centre support.
14 Shape and fasten knee for king plank.
15 Fit king plank. Order rigging and blocks and ballast (paint the ballast with bitumastic paint as soon as you get it).
16 Shape and fit lodging knees to forward bulkhead beam.
17 Fit cabin carlings into position, marking where the side deck beams are to come and cutting slots for them in the carlings.

18 Make side deck beams and fit.
19 Make and fit after bulkhead uprights, cross beams, door frames, etc.
   Shape and fit lodging knees between shelf and bulkhead beams.
20 Fit cockpit carlings.
21 Prime all new woodwork as fitted. If bulkhead rail is being fitted, shape
   and fasten timbers now, plank and fit capping.
22 Plank deck.
23 Fit cabin trunk sides.
24 Fit cabin trunk, forward bulkhead beams and knees.
25 Mark up and slot for roof beams. Fit and prime.
26 Cut ports or windows.
27 Panel cabin bulkhead. Fit ports or windows.
28 Plank cabin trunk roof.
29 Canvas deck and cabin top. Paint canvas as soon as laid.
30 Paint deck and cabin bulkheads, etc. If installing an engine, do so now,
   before completing the cockpit.
31 Make and fit cockpit lockers and coaming.
32 Make doors for cabin and cupboards.
33 Make and fit side benches.
34 Order ground tackle.

Outside work
 1 Make rudder and tiller and fit gudgeons.
 2 Fit pintles and hang rudder.
 3 Make bitts.
 4 Paint topsides.
 5 Make bowsprit step and fit bobstay.
 6 Make main mast, rig and step; set up rigging, make and fit boom and
   gaff. Fix necessary cleats and ring-bolts.
 7 Make, rig and set up mizzen mast.
 8 Make and fit boom crutches.
 9 Fit hawsepipe and make anchor chocks.
10 Bend sails.
11 Antifoul bottom.

Inside work
 1 Make chain locker.
 2 Make bunk framing and tops.
 3 Frame galley and panel.

4 Make cupboards.
5 Install ballast.
6 Finish inside painting.

The installation of the engine will depend on circumstances. If possible, install before completing bulkhead, painting, etc.

Steel lifeboats
It is idle to pretend that for most people converting a steel hull is not a more difficult undertaking than the conversion of a wooden hull. However, if you are confident you have the skills to work in sheet steel, the steel work can still stop at deck level. Plywood decks can be fitted to wooden beams, dovetailed into a wooden shelf which will be bolted to the steel hull at or below the gunwale level. Raised topsides can also be of wood.

If the boat is to sail, you will have to fit a false keel and stiffen the hull with either steel webs or wooden floors. The keel itself can be of wood through-bolted to wood floors, or if a ballast keel, it can be cast in concrete, either between welded plates or reinforced lengthwise with steel rods and cast in wooden shuttering. In either case it will be held in position with bolts to the floors. There is more about this in Chapter 8.

When installing engines in steel hulls, support on steel angle-iron bearers 3 in. by 3 in. by $\frac{1}{4}$ in. and do not drill for the stern tube through the sternpost, but to one side. For details of such installations see Chapter 3.

A final point about steel hulls is that the hulls need a lot of preparation before and during painting. All rust and scale must be removed from the hull, both inside and out, before painting. For this you need a chipping hammer and a wire brush. Quite hard blows may be needed to shift some areas of scale and rust. Below the waterline, use a black bituminous paint. Max Gunning (Dutch yacht designer in steel) used ordinary coal tar from local gas works for the inside below the waterline. This is relatively cheap. For above the waterline, use zinc chromate paint. Just as much attention should be paid to the inside of the hull as to the outside. If the inside is to be wood lined, I suggest you use bituminous paint for the whole of the inside of the hull. When painting, put the priming coat on first and then with the liberal use of Polyfiller or similar trowel cement set about ironing out all the uneven patches. This Polyfiller needs a good key in the priming coat to make it hold, otherwise great sheets of the material can peel away.

With a wood shelf, wooden deck beams and floors, the fitting of the bulkheads, cabin trunks, etc. is exactly the same as in wooden hulls. It may be necessary to weld on lugs or angle brackets to the steel hull, for attachment points for linings, etc. Minor repairs on steel hulls can be made with glass fibre.

Glassfibre lifeboats

Fibreglass is a misnomer for the material used in modern boat building. As Hugo du Plessis makes clear in his most useful book* on this subject, the better name would be reinforced plastic, for glassfibre mat is only about 25 per cent of the content of this material, the other 75 per cent usually being a polyester resin. Glass reinforced plastic (GRP) is the term used by Lloyds, but the average yachtsman is going to go on calling it 'fibreglass' in spite of that. The essence of the process is a catalytic action on a resin causing the curing or polymerisation, and so the hardening of the resin.

The polyester resin is a syrupy liquid to which has been added an accelerator. The accelerator is the ingredient that causes the resin to set cold (i.e. at normal room temperature). The catalyst, which is a special peroxide, is the agent that you (the operator) add to the resin, to cause it to harden. Resins can be bought already coloured or you can add colour yourself, with the mixing of proprietary coloured pastes made up for this purpose.

GRP *construction methods*

In building a GRP boat you have to start with a mould which must have a clean surface. This could be a clinker-built wooden dinghy, in which case it must have a perfectly clean surface, well polished with a wax polish. The mould has to be covered with some anti-stick agent so that the GRP can be freed after the casting (a poly-vinyl-alcohol emulsion, painted on very thinly). After mixing the resin and the catalyst, the first coat of resin (the gel coat) is then painted onto the mould. This is followed by a second coat of resin, then the glass mat is laid on and pressed into the resin so that it is thoroughly impregnated with it. Another resin coat is applied to this and then another layer of glass mat and so on. Meanwhile the catalytic action is at work and curing will continue for 48 hours. The GRP is then ready for removal from the mould, for attachment if it is only a small part, or for finishing if it is the mould for a complete hull.

When buying a used GRP hull, crazing of the surface, as in the glaze of an old piece of pottery, and hairline cracks can be an indication of poor production. Such cracks may lead to leaks in double skin boats such as some glassfibre dinghies. Minor crazing and scratches are unimportant and can be

----

Fibreglass Boats, Hugo du Plessis. Adlard Coles, London, and John de Graff, N.Y., 1964. See also *It's a Stick-up*, Dermott Wright. *Motor Boat and Yachting*, 9 Jan. 1970, London

dealt with by sandpapering and the use of resin or polyurethane fillers. An ex-lifeboat built of GRP is certain to need painting. To do this, the whole surface should be sandpapered, but NOT with a power sander, because the heat from the friction will soften the GRP. Sandpapering will give it a key to which the paint can adhere. Either oil-based or polyurethane-based paints can be used. The latter are more expensive, but will last about three times as long. Antifouling can be of any kind.

In working on a glassfibre hull, treat it gently. You can saw, file or drill GRP, but you cannot hammer it, for it will fracture. Any fitting that will have any tension on it (cleats, bollards, ring-bolts) must be through-fastened to a pad of hard wood. Cleats, ring-bolts on metal plates, etc. should also be separated from the surface with a soft gasket or washer, or bedded down in Sealastic. If you screw such fittings to the GRP alone you get delamination; if you bolt them you get distortion. Likewise, when riveting use over-large rooves (or washers) or use pop-rivets: these are hollow rivets which have to be fitted with a special tool that obviates the need for hammering.

Bonding wood to GRP

The recommended practice for joints for both GRP to GRP and wood to GRP are described in detail, with much else of value to the converter in *Fibreglass Boats*. In brief, it is possible to bond (i.e. stick) wood to GRP by soaking the wood with resin, using a special thinner for the purpose. Do not use wood preservatives on the wood as some of these set up a reaction with the polyester resins. The resins themselves act as a wood preservative. The glassfibre hull must be sandpapered clean and degreased by using acetone, but use this somewhat sparingly, for it softens the surface. Tufnol can also be bonded to GRP but its surface needs roughing up to give it a key. Bonding metal to GRP is not very satisfactory and will not work at all with polished metals such as stainless steel.

Using tools on GRP

When drilling glassfibre, always drill through on the smooth side. Sawing, use fine-toothed saws, either a hacksaw or a padsaw, with not less than 26 teeth to the inch. File with a medium coarse, open-pattern file, again working away from the smooth surface. For sandpapering use only wet and dry sandpaper with plenty of water or white spirit. Immediately after use clean your tools with acetone.

Repairs

Repairs to minor holes or splits can easily be made by application of glass mat and polyester resin to the hole or split, which must be backed with a piece of plywood bent to the curve of the boat. This ply backing piece should be covered in polythene so that it can be freed after the mat and the resin have set. Continue to make further applications of the mat and resin until the hole is filled. Proprietary polyester putty can be used for scratches and shallow scrapes.

Decks and bulkheads

One of the major jobs in converting a glassfibre lifeboat into a cruising yacht is of course fitting the deck to the glassfibre hull. If, as it probably will be, it is a plywood deck, then it must have a shelf, either wooden or moulded, to support it and to carry its deck beams. A wooden shelf, wooden beams and marine ply would make the most easily constructed deck for such a craft. The wooden shelf will have to be screwed or bolted to the moulded frames of the hull. It can be further secured by moulded angles.

In fitting bulkheads it is necessary to spread the impact of the edge of the bulkhead, otherwise it will cause a visible bulge in the topsides. Convert the sharp edge of the bulkhead into a T-shape by using matting or some form of padding at least 3 in. wide, to support a mat on both sides of the bulkhead.

Engine installation

Bearers must be substantial and of suitable length. They must not be through-bolted to the outside of the hull. Whether the bearers are to be of wood, metal, or glassfibre section frames with wooden cores, they must be fastened to the hull with large matted-in webs or angles. The greater the spread of the bearers the better, for they will absorb the vibration of the engine before it reaches the hull.

When fitting the stern tube, it is as well to mould in a substantial shaft log (a block of wood) to take the full length of the stern tube and also to help stiffen the stern of the boat. As heat melts GRP, exhaust pipes must be separated from the glassfibre hull with a length of asbestos tape, bound in with a layer of glass cloth. The same kind of lagging would of course be needed for a stove chimney, if you are installing a coal or charcoal stove.

Shroud plates, ballast and tanks

Earthing against static electricity is essential. Both the metal parts of the fuel system, including the filler pipes and those connected with the engine, must be electrically bonded together and earthed.* If this is not done, static charges of electricity may cause sparks which in their turn may cause disastrous fires. This bonding is simply a matter of connecting up with wire the different parts so that they are all maintained at the same potential. Earthing should be to a metal plate of not less than 36 sq. in. fitted outside the hull below the waterline.†

Shroud plates should be wide (plate shaped) rather than the normal long strips of metal. They should be through-fastened to the shelf. This is of course to spread the load and to take it away from the topsides. The space between the shelf and the glassfibre hull should be filled at this point with a pad of wood.

Ballast keels are hardly suitable for this type of boat, so use internal ballast, which could well be of concrete, perhaps mixed with small pieces of scrap iron, such as old furnace bars.

Tanks for fuel or water can be moulded in glassfibre. Use five layers of $1\frac{1}{2}$ oz. mat for water and 7 layers of $1\frac{1}{2}$ oz. mat for fuel. Do not attempt to bond in fuel pipes to the tanks, but use proprietary threaded pipe fittings which are secured by nuts. They can be of metal of polythene for water tanks.

Sheathing a boat in GRP

There are obvious advantages in sheathing a wooden hull with glass reinforced plastics. It makes the hull waterproof, apart from any leaks through the stern gland; it provides protection from wood-borers and will add strength to the hull. Hulls up to 26 ft overall should be 'sheathed with polyester resin, reinforced by a glass fabric. For larger hulls, this becomes rather expensive, so sheathe with woven rovings, which will also produce a thicker skin.

Before starting work on sheathing a hull, it should be thoroughly dry and all repairs completed. If one is planning to sheathe a ship's lifeboat or any other small craft and this decision has been taken before any conversion work starts, apart from false keels, sternposts, etc., then turn the hull upside down. This makes the work much simpler. In the case of wooden keels, iron keel bands or ballast keels should be removed, as should rubbing strakes or other protective pieces. The surface of the hull should then be sanded, *using a portable disc sander with coarse grit*. This will not only effectively strip off the old paint, but will still leave a surface with sufficient

* *Fibreglass Boats*
† *ibid*

key for the resin. Seams should be raked out and any oil contamination removed by the use of carbon tetrachloride. After sanding, any scratches or scores should be filled in with plastic wood or resin putty.

The glass cloth can now be laid down, either on the tacky surface of the hull which has been coated with resin, or onto the dry hull and a very liberal coating of resin can then be applied on top of the glass mat and allowed to soak through to the wood. In this method, as the resin soaks into the wood, it draws more resin through the glass mat and positively sucks the mat down onto the hull.

For carvel planking, work from the keel outwards to the topsides; for clench (lapstrake) planking, because of the lands, work from the deck line towards the keel. In the case of clench planking it is advisable to do it plank by plank, covering one plank before moving on to the next. At the stem and sternposts, overlap the glass mat.

Further layers of sheathing can then be put on. For most purposes, three layers should be enough. When the sheathing is complete, the entire hull should be lightly sanded (by hand), screw heads should be filled in with resin putty and then the final coat of polyester resin applied. This last varnish coat can be coloured (see page 41). It is important that only the outside of the timber hull should be sheathed for wood must breathe.*

Painting

In the case of old wooden hulls, either burn off all the old paint or strip it off with a good non-caustic paint remover, or borrow a portable disc sander. If you have never used one of these before, practice on something that does not matter, such as old locker fronts or floorboards. Always leave a key (i.e. a not too smooth surface) on each undercoat; use the best possible paint brushes and, after use, wash them out in whatever solvent or thinner you are using and then give them a final wash in hot soapy water and hang them up to dry.

Priming coats

These are necessary only when you are using new wood or have stripped the old wood bare. Modern primers for the hulls of wooden boats are made up of a water repellent varnish and a pigment containing aluminium powder. This is what gives this brownish paint a metallic sheen. It is tough and elastic, and most important, it is water resistant and won't blister.

* Acknowledgement for the information contained in these notes about sheathing a hull with GRP is due to the Reinforcements Division of Fibreglass Ltd, Bidston Birkenhead England

For priming the steel hulls of lifeboats, which are almost certainly either galvanised or zinc-sprayed, use bitumen-based paint for below the waterline and zinc chromate paints for above. These primers are specially manufactured for the purpose. Glassfibre hulls do not need priming.

Undercoating
For a really superb finish, you may have to apply three or four separate undercoats with careful rubbing down between each one. This rubbing down should always leave an adequate key for the next coat to adhere to. Paint each new coat as soon as the previous one is dry enough to stand rubbing down. Undercoats should be painted on generously. They consist of pigment bound up with a little varnish.

Top coating
The final coat is an enamel made up of pigment and weather resistant varnish. It should be applied evenly and thinly, always finishing up with fore and aft brushed strokes. Where paint abuts varnish, or two different colours abut, use masking tape to give a clean line.

6 *Tamaroa*, 28 ft lifeboat ketch with false bow and foredeck view of false bow

Synthetic resin paints

These are more expensive than oil-based paints, but have better lasting qualities. Some of them are more trouble to put on, particularly the 'two can' varieties, and they all have their own special thinners. Polyurethane paints are the easiest of the synthetics to apply. They are highly resistant to seawater and keep their gloss. They can be thinned with white spirit. Epoxide resin paints are also not difficult to use and last quite well, but show evidence of chalking after a season's wear.

Deck paints

The essential thing about a deck paint is that it should be non-slip. I always use a brick red paint which is manufactured for the decks of East Coast trawlers. This is not slippery; it slowly wears away retaining a fresh, if slightly chalky surface. Such paints have the minimum amount of varnish in them. One should be prepared to paint one's deck more than once in a season.

Antifouling

It is most difficult to give good advice on this matter, for so much depends on the area in which the boat is to be kept and the type of fouling likely in that area. The essence of an antifouling paint is that it is poisonous (mercuric or cupric oxides) and that it leaches away during the season, so permitting the poisons to act. Antifouling should be painted on in one coat, as thickly as possible, just before launching or between tides. It can be very costly stuff and if you don't want to spend your money in this way, just use black tar varnish and be prepared to scrub the bottom of your boat once a month. I have used this. I remember once that for two years the tarred bottom of my boat remained absolutely clean and in the third year it grew a great coat of barnacles in six weeks.

Brightwork

If you don't want to spend too much time maintaining your boat, you should limit your varnished areas to the minimum. Good preparation of the surface is essential. The wood should then be primed with varnish thinned down with 10 per cent of turpentine. This will seal the grain and also cause it to rise up slightly, so further rubbing down with fine sandpaper is essential. Synthetic varnishes need some care in their application, but they

7 Clamps are essential

have three times the life of ordinary varnishes. Polyurethane varnish can be applied on rubbed-down ordinary varnish. In cold weather place the varnish can in another and larger can of hot water.

The boot-topping

This can wait until the boat is rigged and ballasted and has had a trial sail to make sure she is in correct trim.

On a perfectly calm day, when the boat is afloat at her moorings, chalk in the waterline by making marks at about 2 ft intervals, and closer at stem and stern. Then put the boat ashore and, with a long batten, draw in a fair curve in chalk on each side. This will be the bottom of the boot, which can be 3 in. deep amidships and 7 in. forward and 5 in. on the after side of the rudder. Again using your batten draw in a fair curve on both sides (make sure that the two sides match). Now paint this with at least three coats of white lead, one of zinc white and one of zinc enamel — the best you can buy, for here between wind and water she will suffer most wear and tear. A well-painted boot-topping will improve her appearance more than anything else.

Rubbing strakes

Lifeboats often have a top strake of mahogany below which is an oak rubbing strake of rounded section. If they are not too damaged, they can be rubbed down and varnished. In the final painting it is worth treating these upper strakes in a different manner from the rest of the topsides.

TWO

Rigging, sails and spars

For conversion and restoration of fishing boats and other sailing craft, the sail and rigging plan may be there for you to use as it is, or to modify as you wish. In the case of ships' lifeboats and the like, you have to start from the beginning, by working out a sail plan. For boats under 25 ft overall, the simpler the rig and the fewer the sails, the better and certainly the cheaper. For larger craft it may be as well to break up the sail plan and to rig the boat as a yawl or a ketch. Certainly my 26 ft lifeboat looked quite handsome with its ketch rig. After roughly sketching out the kind of rig that you think would suit your conversion, you can then get down to the job of working the sail plan out properly.

It used to be said that the amount of sail needed to drive a large yacht was approximately 100 sq. ft for every ton of displacement. To assess the displacement of a lifeboat in cubic feet multiply the waterline length of the boat by the beam by the draught by 0·4 (the block coefficient). So for a lifeboat of 26 ft WL, one arrives at these figures: 26 ft × 8 ft × 2 ft × 0·4 = 166·4 cu. ft. As 35 cu. ft of seawater = 1 ton, divide this figure by 35 and you will arrive at the displacement tonnage. In the case of this lifeboat $\frac{166·4}{35}$ = 4·76.

Fig. 6 The sail plan of a BoT ship's lifeboat

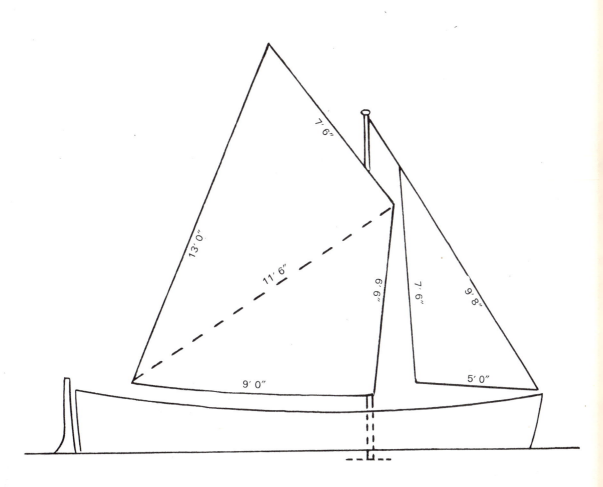

She will need 476 sq. ft for completely effective sail power in light airs. For normal conditions round the coasts of Britain, 80 per cent of this figure is nearer the mark. Our 26 ft overall lifeboat (approx 24 ft WL) had 375 sq. ft, which is just under 80 per cent of 476 sq. ft and was enough for anything but light airs.

For drawing sail plans, or any other plans, you need a large drawing board or flat surface, a T-square, two set squares (60° and 45°), a scale ruler, HB pencils, rubbers and smooth cartridge paper. Work either 1 in. = 1 ft or $\frac{3}{4}$ in. = 1 ft or $\frac{1}{2}$ in. = 1 ft. For curves have one or two long flexible wooden battens, which can be held in position with pins or weights. For a sail plan $\frac{1}{2}$ in.= 1 ft scale is large enough. In working out a sail plan for a double-ended hull like a lifeboat, there is considerable tolerance in the position of the mast(s) and sails. The use of the gaff rig makes it even simpler as there is much more latitude in the rig for the relative positions of centre of effort and centre of lateral resistance. Also, for heavy hulls like fishing boats, do not be tempted by the apparent simplicity of the bermudan rig. Such a rig lacks the drive necessary to push the deep-draft fishing boat hull through the water.

In working out a sail plan, the centre of effort (CE) of the sails must be forward of the centre of lateral resistance (CLR) of the hull. To find the CLR, cut out the underwater profile in a sheet of stiff paper or card and balance it on a knife edge. The point of balance is the CLR. I wish it was as easy to assess the centre of effort of the sail plan.

To measure sail area
Triangular sails (headsails and bermudan main or mizzen): from any corner drop a vertical to the opposite side. The area of the sail equals in square feet this opposite side (the base line) multiplied by half the vertical. For a gaff main, divide the sail into two triangles and work out in the same way, adding the areas of the two triangles to give the area of the gaff sail.

To assess the centre of effort
It is almost impossible to explain this in words. However this diagram, which was worked out by the American naval architect Howard I. Chapelle, goes some way to making it understandable.*
1 In the mainsail draw diagonals AB and CD, to intersect at point E. Make
   BF = AE and DH = CE. Draw in the line FH. Points O and P are the

* *Yacht Designing and Planning*, Howard I. Chapelle, Norton, New York, 1936

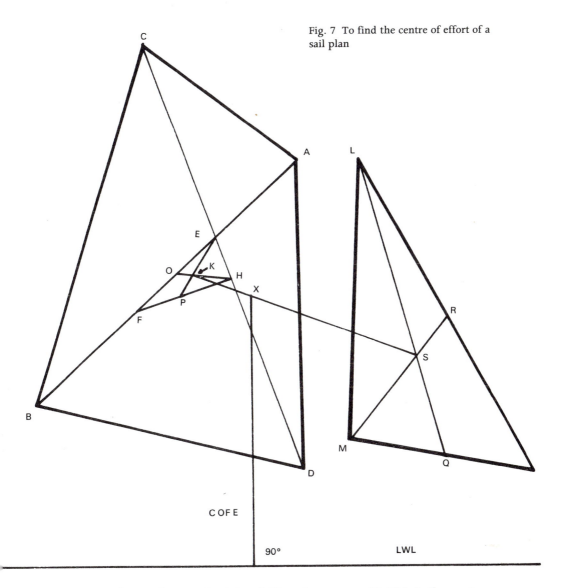

Fig. 7 To find the centre of effort of a sail plan

centres of FE and FH. Join OH and EP to intersect at Y. This is the centre of effort of the mainsail.

2 In the jib, draw straight lines from any two corners (say L and M) to the mid-points of the opposite side (say Q and R). They intersect at point S which is the centre of effort of the jib.

3 Now join the centre of these two sails to make line KS. Multiply the area of the jib by the scale length in feet of KS, divided by the sum of the areas of the mainsail and jib. This gives the scale distance in feet of the CE (point X) of the total area from the CE of the main sail (point K).
4 For ketches and yawls, the common CE of say jib and main is found and then reckoned as if for one sail area and computed in combination with the mizzen.
5 Drop a vertical to waterline to show position of CE in relation to CLR.

In the case of a 26 ft lifeboat, the centre of effort should be about 9 or 10 in. forward of the centre of lateral resistance. In the case of a centreboard boat, such as the whaler, the centre of the lateral plane should be taken when the centreboard is about two-thirds down.

Bermudan and gaff rigs; ropes and wire rigging
The now almost universal bermudan rig, which looks so simple, is in many ways more difficult for the amateur builder and designer. The mast has to be longer and lighter, so it can no longer be an ex-scaffold pole. It has to be lighter, so it must be hollow. It has to withstand heavy compression strains and it cannot be allowed to bend, so it has to be stronger and to be rigged with spreaders and stays.

Hollow masts: wood
With an adequate workshop space, hollow masts are not too difficult to make. The simplest kind of hollow mast is a long tapering square wooden box. An alternative is to make it up from two long planks whose total thickness equals the fore-and-aft measurement of the spar. The insides can then be hollowed and the outsides shaped and tapered. Both box and hollow plank masts will need strengthening where mast bands, shroud tangs or spreader sockets come. This is best done by fitting solid chocks of wood to fill the hollow of the mast at these points. The whole assembly can then be glued up with water-resistant phenol-formaldehyde glues. These are preferable to casein powder glues, which are not impervious to water.

If, as is highly probable, you cannot get adequate lengths of timber (well seasoned Sitka spurce or Norway pine), you will have to make your two halves, or the four sides of your box spars, with more than one length of plank. These should be glued together with long scarphs.

It is not possible to raise a bermudan mainsail, fixed to hoops or lacing, up a mast encumbered with spreaders, so a track on the after side of the mast is essential. To travel up this track the luff rope of the mainsail is fastened to a number of slides that fit into the track and are free to slide up or down. The sail needs only a single halyard at the head.

The type of track most commonly used is C or channel sectioned. Where one length of track joins the next the butting edges must be smoothed off or rounded with a file, so that the slides have nothing on which to catch. Whenever possible, shackle the slides to the luff cringles. Seizings can easily chafe through and break.

In the case of small boats, it is possible to dispense with the track and slides and to run the luff rope up inside a hollow groove cut in the mast, but the opening must be made wide enough so that the sail does not stick, but not wide enough for the luff rope to pull out.

Hollow masts: aluminium alloy
The modern alternatives to wooden masts are of course those built of aluminium alloy. These are not something that the handyman can knock up for himself. If your conversion is essentially a sailing boat such as, for example, an old Six-metre or a Clyde cruising Eight-metre or even a Montagu whaler, the proprietory brands of hollow alloy masts are the best solution if you can afford the price. The reliability of these spars is proved by their use on ocean racers and by their use in such a boat as Sir Alec Rose's *Lively Lady*. Manufacturers of these spars, such as Ian Proctor Metal Masts Ltd, Swanwick, Southampton, or Sparlight Ltd, Southbourne, Emsworth, Hampshire, make as many as 400 aluminium alloy masts a week. That kind of experience and know-how is not something an amateur can pick up in a few weekends. Such firms provide a wide range of stock masts, so it need not be a matter of custom building. Also the complete standing and running rigging can be made up for you. The sparring and rigging of a bermudan-rigged boat cannot be done on the cheap. This is a highly sophisticated rig, hence the sense in using gaff rig for most conversions.

Gaff rig
Jibs and foresails need only a single halyard, but to obtain a taut luff, which is of vital importance for windward work, the fitting of a downhaul for each foresail is certainly worth while. Downhauls usually consist of a wire tackle hooked onto a pendant at the foot of the sail and leading through a block at the stemhead or bowsprit end. The downhaul is made fast to a cleat on the deck. All one has to do is to run the sail up, make fast the halyard and then take up the slack on the downhaul where one can get a much better purchase than on the halyard.

Boomed foresails

The advantage of a boomed foresail means that the sail can be left to look after itself when going about, for its sheets can run through a block shackled to a horse or a track on the foredeck. The ends of the sheet are led aft and made fast to cleats on either side of the cockpit. These are adjusted only if you want to let the sail out a little more or to harden it in. Boomed foresails should be loose footed. The disadvantages of this sail are that it does not set so well and it cannot overlap the main. It is a little less in area than a normal sheeted foresail.

Mainsail

The traditional mainsail has a gaff of at least two-thirds the length of the boom. Such a spar needs more than one halyard to keep it under control. Hence the throat and peak halyards. To get adequate purchase on the throat halyard it is probably necessary to make it up with a luff tackle. For the peak halyard a tackle can be worked in to support the gaff. The Dutch rig with a loose-footed mainsail has a short curved gaff. I have used this rig on my present boat for the last ten years. It is most effective. The mainsail has a long leading edge and the gaff is only 6 ft 6 in. long, whereas the boom is 14 ft long. My gaff is actually rigged with throat and peak halyards but it is quite feasible to rig this spar and sail with only one halyard.

The final variation on the gaff rig is to have a boomless mainsail. This used to be used in fishing boats, such as Thames bawleys, where the boom would be in the way of the trawl. It is a less weatherly rig and the main sheet block, uncontrolled by any boom, can become a pretty lethal thing if it starts flailing about when the boat is in stays or when reefing. If fitted with brailing lines it provides a very handy rig as one can brail up the mainsail when coming to anchor or when about to ride out a short-lived but heavy squall.

Sails

For conversions, where one is hoping to retain something of the character of traditional craft, and certainly for any restorations of old fishing boats, cotton or flax sails are preferable to synthetic materials. Terylene would be completely out of character on an old oyster smack or a Dutch botter, but is the obvious answer for whaler or lifeboat conversions. For Terylene weights, etc., consult a sailmaker.

Egyptian cotton used to be specified for all good quality yacht sails. Today it is unobtainable, for it is no longer made up in weights suitable for this purpose. Most of the cotton now used comes from the USA or Canada, though there is some cotton sailcloth imported from Hong Kong. Cotton sailcloth is designated by ounce weight per yard run, which may be 24 in., $28\frac{1}{2}$ in. or 36 in. wide. The latter two widths are much the more common. Flax is designated with numbers 00, 0, 1, 2, 3, 4 and so on. 00 is the heaviest. It is difficult to give comparative measurements; the only thing to do is to consult your sailmaker. The price of both materials is very much the same, but they have different characteristics. Cotton sails keep their shape much better than flax ones *but* flax is tougher, it is more resistant to mildew and is much easier to handle when wet, for flax is soft when wet whereas cotton sailcloth can become as hard as a board.

The specification for the sails for *Lilian*, a 32 ft bawley with a 685 sq. ft sail area, were:

Mainsail No. 4 flax, 2 rows reef points and brail cringle
Topsail 10 oz. cotton 10/28 – 12 oz. 36
Foresail No. 4 flax
Working jib 10 oz. cotton 10/28

Sailmakers and sailors disagree about whether to dress cotton or flax sails as soon as they are made or after a season's sailing. On the whole I would think it is better to dress the sails after a season's sailing, so that the fibres of cotton or flax may be allowed to stretch. This does not apply to Terylene. Dressings used include fish oil and ochre, which the Thames barges always use. It has a lovely rich red colour, but it never dries and it comes off on everything. It is uniquely effective in preserving flax or cotton sails that are left out in all weathers, but it does make the sails very heavy.

Writing some 60 years ago, Claud Worth, in his book *Yacht Cruising*, gave the following recipe for a sail dressing:

Put in a copper, 5 gallons of best raw linseed oil and $1\frac{1}{4}$ lb. of beeswax. Heat until it begins to boil, then gradually add 20 lb. of Venetian red ochre and 10 lb. 'light purple brown' ochre, and boil for five minutes, stirring all the time. When cool enough add 10 gallons of best paraffin. Spread the dry sails on a clean floor or clean shingle beach. Keep the contents of the copper constantly stirred. Brush it on both sides of the sails with a large paint scrubber, working the mixture well into the tablings . . . they should be hung up to dry in an open shed.

Cutch tanning, which is made from the bark of an Eastern tree (*Acacia catechu*) is an effective preservative for both cotton and flax. It is difficult to

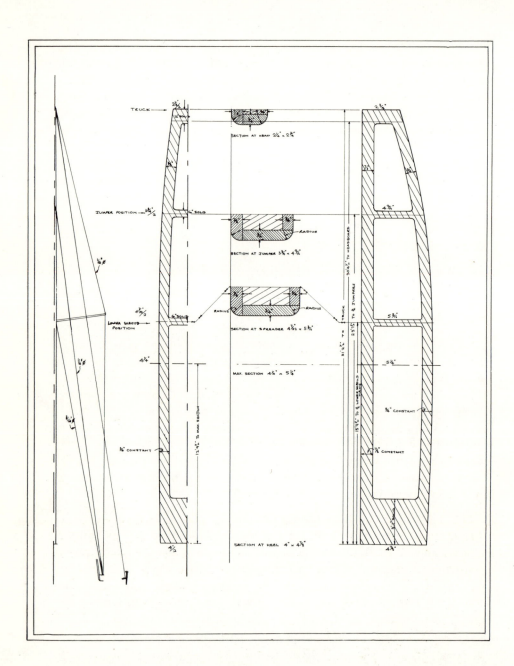

Fig. 8 The construction of hollow masts

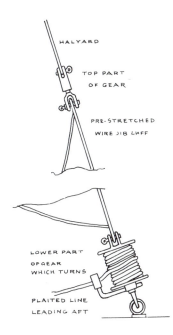

HALYARD

TOP PART
OF GEAR

PRE-STRETCHED
WIRE JIB LUFF

LOWER PART
OF GEAR
WHICH TURNS

PLAITED LINE
LEADING AFT

Fig. 9 Wykeham-Martin furling gear

apply, for you have to have a tank big enough to take your mainsail as the cutch has to be boiled in water. Until recently it was possible to have sails cutch tanned in England by one or two firms who made sails for fishing boats, but no longer. I do not recommend you to try cutching.

There are now proprietary dressings on the market that are more effective and far easier to use. One of these is Kanvo. It is not cheap, but it is effective and can be bought colourless or in various colours. Sails are now so expensive, it obviously behoves one to look after them. For instance, always slacken the outhauls when the sails are to be stowed, for the ropes at the foot of the sail absorb more dampness than the furled canvas. Never furl a wet sail, but bundle it up loosely, so that the air can circulate; and never put a sail cover over a wet sail. At the end of the season, wash your sails in fresh water, either with a hose or in a bathtub.

Italian hemp bolt ropes should every year or so be given a dressing of Stockholm tar. This should be warmed and then brushed in well with a stiff brush. It is worth doing just for the smell, which is evocative of every sail loft in the world. Incidentally, Stockholm tar is a wood tar and has nothing to do with coal tar. It can be bought from sailmakers.

The luff ropes of headsails will nearly always be of flexible galvanised wire 6×12, and vinyl covered. If you are using Wykeham-Martin gear, then specify 7×7.

Wykeham-Martin jib furling gear

This gear makes it possible to furl headsails as if they were on a roller. The gear is in two parts: the top part is a gunmetal swivel that is shackled to the jib halyard and the head of the sail; the lower part consists of a gunmetal reel or flanged roller shackled to the stemhead, bowsprit end or traveller. A plaited line is wound a number of times round the collar, and with the jib halyards set up really taut (this is essential if there is any weight in the wind) a pull on this line will wind the sail round itself. A pull on one of the sheets will unwind it.

The gear is made in four different sizes and can be bought from yacht chandlers and sailmakers. Size 1 is for a sail of 40 ft, size 2 for 85 ft, size 3 for 150 ft and size 4 for 230 ft. It is a most valuable piece of equipment for sailing singlehanded, but it is *not a reefing gear*. The sail will not stay only partly unrolled; it is either fully furled or fully set. It may be tempting to leave the sails in position, rolled up, but in time they will rot along the exposed part. It is advisable to unhitch them and stow below in the ordinary way.

Fig. 10 *Left*: Wooden block. *Right*:
Block stropped and with thimble seized
in position

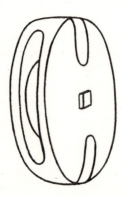

Ropes

Halyards	8-plait or 3-strand pre-stretched Terylene. (The use of 8-plait prevents twist in jib luffs.)		
Boats 21–30 ft 4–7 tons	Main $1\frac{1}{8}$ in. circum. Jib $1\frac{1}{8}$ in. Yankee or spinnaker $\frac{7}{8}$ in. Signal $\frac{3}{8}$ in. plaited	Boats 31–40 ft 10 tons	Main $1\frac{1}{4}$ in. Jib $1\frac{1}{4}$ in. Yankee or spinnaker $\frac{7}{8}$ in. Signal $\frac{3}{8}$ in. plaited
Sheets Boats 21–30 ft	3-strand Terylene will wear best Main $1\frac{1}{4}$ in. circum. Jib $1\frac{1}{4}$ in. Genoa $1\frac{1}{4}$ in. Spinnaker $1\frac{1}{4}$ in.	Boats 31–40 ft	Main $1\frac{1}{2}$ in. Jib $1\frac{1}{2}$ in. Genoa $1\frac{3}{4}$ in. Spinnaker $1\frac{3}{4}$ in.
Anchor warps	3-strand Terylene or multi-plait nylon (stretches, so absorbs shock, which is useful) with 2 fathoms of chain at anchor end.		
Boats 21–30 ft	Chain $\frac{5}{16}$ in. Rope 2 in. CQR 30 lbs. Kedge rope 1 in.		
Boats 31–40 ft	,, $\frac{3}{8}$ in. ,, $2\frac{1}{2}$ in. ,, 43 lbs. ,, ,, $1\frac{1}{4}$ in.		
Mooring ropes	3-strand Terylene		
Boats 21–30 ft	$1\frac{1}{2}$ in.		
Boats 31–40 ft	$1\frac{3}{4}$ in.		

Use Terylene whipping twine.

Using Terylene means that you can dispense with wire for halyards. Pre-stretched Terylene halyards are processed to reduce elasticity. They stretch slightly more than wire, so need hardening up—but are more weatherproof, flexible and last longer. At the time of writing $1\frac{1}{4}$ in. Terylene retails at 5p per foot. Also, you do not have to splice on rope tails to the wire halyards.

Wire rigging
If expense is not too important a matter, use stainless steel wire. However, for most conversion work I would recommend using galvanised wire rope. The most commonly used wire ropes are: 6×7, 7×7 or 1×19.
6×7 has six strands of seven wires laid up round a hemp core
7×7 ,, ,, ,, ,, ,, ,, ,, ,, ,, ,, seven-wire centre.
1×19 has nineteen strands of single wires laid up together. It is stronger than either 6×7 or 7×7 and has less stretch.

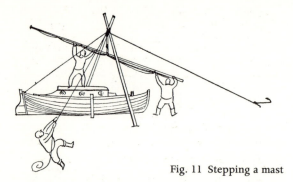

Fig. 11 Stepping a mast

Bobstay

For a bobstay use chain, galvanised $\frac{1}{4}$ in., $\frac{5}{16}$ in. or, for heavier craft (over 10 tons), $\frac{3}{8}$ in. To prevent chafe or the aggravating noise of an anchor or mooring chain grinding against the lower part of the bobstay, cover it with about 4 ft of 1 in. polythene tubing.

Sail covers

Do not use Terylene covers for canvas sails as Terylene will trap condensation. For Terylene sails, of course, it does not matter of what the cover is made.

Runners

Runners are adjustable backstays. In most conversions they are probably an unnecessary nuisance. If the shrouds have an adequate spread and the after shroud is not less than 2 ft astern of the mast, runners are not necessary. If you do fit them, they should lead as far aft as the tack of the jib is forward of the mast. The most effective way of setting up a runner is with the use of a lever. (The Highfield lever is a proprietary brand.) However, for the last ten years I have used a single tackle on my own boat. The block at the foot of the tackle is hooked into an eyebolt in the covering board and the fall is made fast to a cleat or to itself. When the runners are not needed they are unhooked and carried forward to the shrouds where they are hooked into another eyebolt. This keeps them out of the way.

Blocks

Blocks are measured by the length of the shell. Buy your blocks too large rather than too small, for apart from man-made fibres, *wet rope swells*. The length of the block should be three times the circumference of the rope. For wire rope, the diameter of the sheave should be five times the circumference of the rope. The best way to treat blocks is to drive out the pins, remove the sheaves, and then soak the shells in linseed oil for at least three weeks. Then hang them up to dry for a couple of months. Grease the pins well before putting back the sheaves. For the first season there is no need to varnish the blocks, but at the end of the year give them a couple of coats of varnish. To strop a block you must first make a wire grommet long enough to go round the block and the thimble. Grease the grommet and parcel it with a strip of cotton or canvas and then serve it with tarry twine. Slip it over the block and the thimble and seize between the thimble and the block with an ordinary flat seizing.

Stepping the masts
If there is no crane available and the mast is too heavy to manhandle, sheerlegs will have to be used. For these, a pair of scaffold poles should be crossed two or three feet from their top ends and strapped together. A block and tackle should be attached to the point where the poles cross. (I have used my mainsheet for this purpose.) A long line should be made fast to the top of the sheerlegs. The sheerlegs should then be placed in position on either side of the boat and just forward of the mast hole. One end of the long line should be made fast to the stern of the boat and the other end to a point well forward of the stem. This could be an anchor bedded in the ground.

Before stepping the masts, all their spider bands, wedges, hounds, sheaves, goosenecks, and strops should be in position. Attach the blocks for the halyards, runners and topping lifts and shackle on the shrouds and stays. Reeve the halyards and lift the mainmast into position. The shrouds and halyards should be frapped to the mast to keep them out of the way. A stout bridle should be fixed to the mast and the tackle hitched onto it. The spar is then hauled up and eased into the mast hole. The sheerlegs have to be high enough to allow sufficient clearance from the point of balance where the bridle is fixed to the bottom of the mast, in order for the mast to enter the mast hole.

Lowering mast gear
Masts that can be lowered add greatly to the cruising range on inland waters. Though one can go from one end of Holland to the other with fixed masts, much time could be saved by having lowering masts. On English waterways, one would get nowhere unless one could drop one's mast.

The most efficient mast-lowering gear is that used on Dutch boats. It con-

sists of a wishbone-shaped galvanised iron pipe support-fulcrum, which is
hinged to steel legs securely bolted to the covering board, on each side of
the boat, level with the mast. The forestay is unshackled and a tackle is
hitched to its end and led over a sheave at the apex of the wishbone. The
mast is then gently lowered, with the wishbone swinging up and acting as a
fulcrum for the tackle. When not in use, the wishbone rests on the deck,
inside the rail, or it can function as part of the pulpit and do duty for guard
rails

A simpler contrivance than the wishbone is a single 8 ft steel tube, with a
$\frac{1}{2}$ in. rod, 6 in. long, welded onto one end and a miniature rowlock welded
into the other. The $\frac{1}{2}$ in. rod slots into a hole in the mast, faced with a steel
plate about 6 in. from the foot. This method has no lateral stability, so
cannot easily be used if the boat is bobbing about in a seaway. It is, however,
a method I use on my own boat and I have found it quite adequate for the
few times in the year that I need to raise or lower the mast. Providing there
is no wind, it is quite possible for one person to raise or lower my 30 ft solid
spruce mast. And two of us have done it, while under way and in the dark!

Tabernacles
A tabernacle, in which the mast is pivoted, can either be set on the deck and
bolted to the deck beams, or it can be bolted onto a square post that rests
on a mast step supported by floors.

Dutch craft such as the hengst on page 243 have the latter kind. To carry
the weight of the hengst's 10 in. diameter mast, this tabernacle is made up
of two 11 in. by 7 in. timbers that are bolted to an 11 in. square post that
rests on a mast step in the bottom of the boat. The 1 in. thick bolt on which
the mast pivots is 5 in. from the top of the tabernacle. When the mast is up
it is held in position by another heavy bolt fixed to plates on either side of
the tabernacle and about 3 in. clear of the deck. A galvanised steel tabernacle need not be nearly so bulky as a wooden one. For masts that are too
heavy to be manhandled, I suggest the pivot bolt should not be less than 18
in. from the foot of the mast. The tabernacle I use in my boat is shown in
Fig. 125. It was made up by a local blacksmith and incorporates a pin rail.
It is bolted to two deck beams and to a heavy wooden pad that fills the space
between these beams. The thrust of the mast is taken by two 1 in. galvanised
tubes that rest on a special floor.

Wheel steering
Handling a ship's wheel for the first time would come more easily to a

motorist than to a yachtsman who had learned to steer with a tiller. The wheel can be made to be almost as sensitive as a tiller, but this does depend on good engineering. Clearly the gears and cables used in wheel steering are going to cause some resistance. This resistance can be minimal if the installation is carefully done.

The cable-sprocket chain and ball-bearing pulleys should be housed internally to avoid rust and corrosion. They should be liberally greased every season and once or twice during the season as well. The size of the sprocket on the back of the wheel governs the mechanical advantage for any given length of rudder yoke. The rudder yoke should have a constant radius with the rudder pintle as the centre of the circle. This is very important and is the only way of ensuring that the cable is under constant tension; without this even tension you get hard or slack spots, causing resistance or even backlash. The pulleys must be securely bolted to the hull and set at the correct alignment for the cable. Care must be taken so that the cable does not foul the rims of the pulley and that it leads off the centre of the pulley. Under way, with no load on it, the cable can be a little slack, but not slack enough to slip off the pulleys, even if guards are fitted to prevent such a happening. A cable drum on the back of the wheel is less effective than a sprocket and chain because of the displacement of the cable from hard-a-port to hard-a-starboard. Also there is the possibility of the cable turns fouling one another, unless the drum is so machined as to be able to take the cable helically. The sprocket also takes up less space and makes for a neater job everywhere. The principle described here is the same as that used in aircraft, so it should be good enough for converted lifeboats, whalers or any other small craft. The pulleys and ball bearings are often obtainable from surplus trading stores.

Masts and rigging: simple mast construction, stepping etc.
Take your sail plan to a good sailmaker and ask his advice.

It is possible to step your masts on deck but the amateur builder might be well advised to step them on the keel or keelson. The mast steps in my 26 ft lifeboat ketch were rectangular boxes fitting over the keelson and with a mortise cut in the top to receive the tenon on the foot of the mast. The mizzen mast housing can be either a simple opening ring of galvanised iron or, as we had, a wooden support fastened to the main horizontal beam of the cabin bulkhead. This merely holds the mizzen mast upright until it is rigged and takes some of the forward thrust when the boat is under sail.

A much better housing for a mizzen mast is what is called a sailing thwart

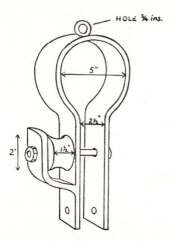

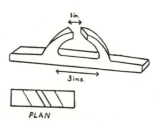

Fig. 13 Fairlead for mooring ropes, cables, etc. The diagonal cut is made, opening up the enclosed fairlead, which is standard on lifeboats

Fig. 12 Gammon iron, with fairlead for cable and ring for forestay

in an open boat and a bridge deck in a cruiser. The space underneath it may be used for lockers or as an engine casing if there is to be an auxiliary. I have redrawn the plans of this conversion to show this.

The bridge deck would consist of two heavy deck beams, the forward one being built into the cabin bulkhead, planked with marine ply or with tongue-and-groove, fore-and-aft just like the deck, but with a heavy centre plank to take the mizzen. With good robust beams the mizzen could be stepped on deck so that the engine could be housed underneath. Vertical 1 in. iron pipes on either side of the engine can take the downward thrust. These supports should be mounted on substantial floors.

Fife rails, bitts
The simplest fife rail is a band round the mast with pins stuck through it. For my 26 ft lifeboat we built a substantial rail with nicely turned oak legs (obtainable ready turned as chair legs from almost any woodworking shop). The halyards led down to small blocks shackled to ring-bolts fitted to the deck close to the mast and then up to the fife rail. Thus the pull on the rail was all in a downward direction, which meant that it could take a great deal of strain without having to be heavily built.

If you do not have a bowsprit you can belay your cable to a samson post instead of to bitts. A samson post is a single piece of timber (4 in. by 4 in. oak, at least) going right down through the king plank to a step on the

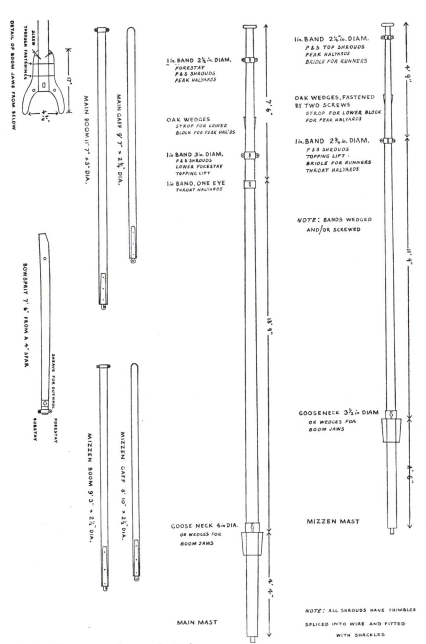

Fig. 14 The masts and spars of a 26 ft lifeboat ketch

keelson; but if there is a bowsprit you will have to moor to bitts. The bitts on smacks and larger boats are usually made like a pair of samson posts and go right down to the bottom of the boat. Bowsprit bitts ought by rights to be carried down to the keel. But if this is impossible, it is better for them to sit on the king plank, with a fastening on to one of the deck beams.

Mast and spars: stripping, shaping, dressing and fitting
The masts and spars for the lifeboat were made from spruce poles, intended for scaffolding. We hung them up horizontally, to dry out, until a couple of months before the boat was to be launched. Then we stripped them with a drawknife, a pleasant and easy tool to use. Holding it with a handle in each hand, you draw it slowly towards you as if it were a giant spokeshave. When all the bark had been stripped off with the drawknife, the spars were planed and rubbed down smooth with sandpaper. Shipwrights usually use a special rounding plane, which is a help but not a necessity. When the spars were smoothed to shape we hung them up again to go on drying out. After a week or so, shakes began to appear. These were of no consequence and later on they would be filled with a soft filling (see page 31). But first we gave the spars a good dressing with hot linseed oil and, when dry, a further dressing with cold.

The masts, if made from grown poles, can follow their natural taper, but with a gaff rig it is better to have a little taper up to the hounds and then quite a marked taper to the truck. A narrow pole at the top will improve the look of a mast and provide a collar for the shrouds and stays, but the whole mast will have to be of heavier timber than if there were a gradual taper. Our masts had no refinements and kept the natural taper of the grown

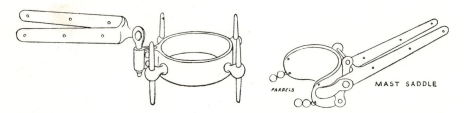

Fig. 15 Spider band fitting and gooseneck, with belaying pins. The side pieces are countersunk into the end of the boom and through-fastened with copper nails and rooves

Fig. 16 Galvanised iron mast saddle, covered with rawhide and held to the mast by parrel balls threaded on galvanised wire

GUNMETAL OR GALVANISED IRON

Fig. 17 Bowsprit traveller

SOLID DROP-FORGED STEEL OPEN BODIES

Fig. 19 Rigging screws

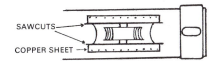

SAWCUTS

COPPER SHEET

Fig. 18 Bowsprit sheave at the outboard
end of the bowsprit, lined with copper

poles. We cut a tenon in the foot for the mast step and in the head for the
truck. You can buy trucks from any ship chandler. Ours were $4\frac{1}{2}$ in. and
4 in. in diameter, and they each had two sheaves for signal halyards. They
make a convenient perch for seagulls.

Shrouds and halyards may be fitted to the masts either by eye-splicing
them round the spar to rest on cheeks, or by shackling them onto strops,
or onto eyes on spider bands.

Ironwork for spars and rigging

The main mast for the 26 ft lifeboat ketch was 25 ft 7 in. long. Sixteen in.
from the truck there was a galvanised iron spider band 1 in. deep and 2 in.
in diameter, to which the shrouds, the peak halyards and the forestay
were shackled. Thirty in. lower down there were two small oak cheeks to
take the strop for the peak halyard block, and 18 in. below them there was
another spider band, of a larger diameter (because of the taper of the mast).
It had four eyes for the lower shrouds, the lower forestay and the topping
lift. Twenty-six in. lower still there was another band with just one eye
for the throat halyards. The gooseneck or the cheeks for the boom jaws
should come 4 ft 5 in. from the foot. A gooseneck is a neater fitting, but
jaws are cheaper. We had jaws.

The mizzen mast was 21 ft long. The top spider band was 9 in. below the
truck, 1 in. deep by $2\frac{1}{2}$ in. in diameter, with four eyes for the shrouds, the

peak halyards and the upper ends of the bridles for the runners (which you may think unnecessary). Twenty-five in. lower are the cheeks for the strip of the lower peak halyard block, and $22\frac{1}{2}$ in. lower still is another spider-band with four eyes, for the shrouds, throat halyards, topping lift, and the lower end of the bridles for the runners. The boom jaw wedges were 4 ft 7 in. from the foot (you may prefer a gooseneck). The booms do not taper and should each have a pair of jaws or a gooseneck fitting. The jaws should be carefully made from substantial straight-grained oak. At the after end, the booms should be finished off with a galvanised iron band, with an eye above and below for the topping lift and the sheet block.

The gaffs were both fitted with the saddle type of jaws, their diameters being 5 in. and 4 in. respectively, and they had 7 in. side pieces. These fittings are not cheap and they have to be lined with leather to prevent chafe; but, if you can afford them, they are far better than wooden jaws, which are an abomination on a gaff, for they are liable to catch the halyards and are also quite likely to break. The gaffs can taper slightly.

If you are fitting a bowsprit, make it a sturdy one. Ours was 7 ft 5 in. long and shaped from a piece of 4 in. by 4 in. spruce. The inboard end was flattened on top and chamfered off aft, to make it a less dangerous obstacle on deck. Outboard it tapered to a diameter of 3 in. and ended in a band with two eyes, the top for the forestay and the lower for the chain bobstay. Inboard of this there is a sheave for the jib outhaul. Any sheaves cut in spars should be coppered. The copper sheet is kept close to the side of the sheave by making saw cuts beyond the opening (Fig. 18). Allow 2 in. for the sheave, 5 in. for the traveller, shackle and splice to the outhaul, and 2 in. of solid timber forward of the sheave mortise; then 3 in. to take the spider band, where the bowsprit should be cut down by about $\frac{1}{2}$ in. in diameter to make a shoulder which will give the spider band good bearing to prevent it drawing aft under the considerable strain it will have to stand. Use a *wrought* iron not a *cast* band. This applies to *all* spider bands.

The remaining fittings for the masts of the gaff rigged 26 ft lifeboat ketch are the mast hoops and the parrels. Wooden hoops 6 in. in diameter can be bought from almost any good nautical ironmonger and are the best sail attachment. Failing wooden hoops, reeve a lanyard. Parrels, the wooden balls on your gaff jaws, should be about 1 in. in diameter. They are threaded on Terylene line which is made very fast to the gaff jaws.

The sizes for the running rigging are $1\frac{1}{2}$ in. circumferences for all halyards and topping lifts and $1\frac{1}{4}$ in. for runners. These ropes are quite large enough, and are easier to handle than smaller sizes. The sheets for the main and mizzen are $1\frac{1}{2}$ in. cotton and $1\frac{1}{4}$ in. for the jib. The shrouds are $\frac{7}{8}$ in. plough steel wire and the bobstay $\frac{1}{4}$ in. chain.

Do not splice thimbles into the lower ends of the stays and shrouds until the mast is stepped, for only then can you find their exact position. When you have put in the splices you can reeve lanyards. If wire splicing is too difficult an undertaking for you, most yacht builders can arrange to have your rigging Talurit spliced.

The chainplates, which incidentally should have been fitted before the side decks were put on, are pieces of galvanised iron strap $\frac{1}{4}$ in. thick by $1\frac{3}{4}$ in. wide, long enough to be fastened through four strakes and to clear the bulwark rail. They are drilled for each fastening and for the shackle at the top; through-fasten them with one $\frac{3}{8}$ in. clench or bolt on each land. They should be fastened right through the lands to substantial wooden chocks inside the planks, and they should be set at the same angle as the rigging so that there is an even and direct pull on them. (See alternative arrangements for glassfibre boats on page 44.)

You may prefer to put the shroud plates inside the planking and bring them up through the capping. This is neater and just as strong, but you must weld a collar to the plate and bed this down on the deck in white lead. Use chain bobstay, never rely on wire; $\frac{5}{16}$ in. short link would be right for this boat. It is not necessary to use a rigging screw; you can set up the stay by heaving down on the bowsprit so that you can shackle the stay with the sprit bent down about $\frac{1}{4}$ in. to $\frac{1}{2}$ in. Use only tested chain and shackles; $\frac{1}{4}$ in. chain is better than wire for bowsprit shrouds, if you have them. I stress the need for strong rigging on the bowsprit, for it sometimes has to stand other than sailing strains.

The simplest bobstay fitting is made by bending a piece of $\frac{1}{2}$ in. iron rod into a U shape, having the two ends forged into eyes to take $\frac{1}{2}$ in. bolts and then galvanising the whole thing. It is bolted through the stem. A neater and more expensive fitting is also shown in Fig. 21. To fit the bobstay, ship the bowsprit and fasten it down inboard. Stand on the outboard end and shackle the chain to the bowsprit end and to the bobstay fitting. This will prevent any sag. Do not make the stay at the end of the bowsprit the only support for the main mast. Have a jib and staysail by all means, but there must be a strong stay from the stemhead with the sail *hanked on*, so that if the bowsprit is carried away, the mast is still safe. It is quite a good idea to have a diagonal reef in the staysail designed to bring the sail down the stay, with the clew still on the same diagonal line as it is when unreefed, so that the lead of the sheet does not alter. The line of reefing points would slope up aft.

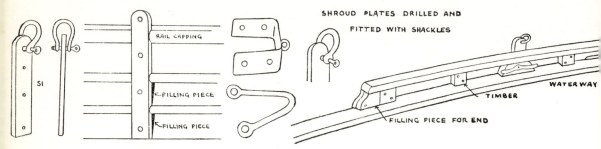

SHROUD PLATES DRILLED AND

FITTED WITH SHACKLES

RAIL CAPPING

FILLING PIECE

FILLING PIECE

TIMBER

WATERWAY

FILLING PIECE FOR END

SI

Figs. 20 & 21 Shroud plates and details.
Bobstay fitting for stem.
Top: Forged fitting with ring welded on.
Bottom: $\frac{1}{2}$ in. iron rod bent to shape

Fig. 22 Bulwark rail, timbers and shroud
plates

Without this reefing device, you would have to have a second, smaller sail.

The strops for the staysail and jib halyard blocks should be long enough to give them plenty of clearance from the mast, so that the fall of the halyard leads clear and does not jam against the mast when the block is forced aft by the strain on the fall. The jib, if set flying, will need only a slight purchase: a wire halyard with a single block with an eye and becket shackled to the fall, and a rope tail spliced into the becket. Hoist the sail with the single part until the block is 5 to 6 ft from the deck, then pass the rope tail under a strong cleat on the mast, reeve it through the block and back to the cleat, thus giving a purchase for the final setting. The staysail could be set with a single part rope halyard and swigged taut, or set in the same way as the jib.

For the mizzen sheets, have double sheets leading down to eyebolts on each side of the deck. On the ketch you will probably already have double sheets for the mainsail, so if it is too much of an encumbrance to have double sheets on the mizzen as well, you can compromise by having a single mizzen sheet running through blocks shackled to eyebolts on each quarter. The sheet leads from the boom through one block, back through a block on a becket at the end of the boom, and through the other quarter block to a cleat.

The tiller is best made of ash. Failing ash, you can use a good piece of oak, preferably with a slight curl to the grain, so that the curve of your tiller can follow the grain of the wood. We made our tiller from a piece of 4 in. by 2 in. oak with a decanter-stopper end. It was cut out with a padsaw and then spokeshaved and planed to shape. If you need a considerable curve on the tiller, it is best to laminate, bending each lamination and glueing up in a jig.

With the mast stepped and standing rigging set up, you can fit the fife rails or pin rails for the halyards. They range from simple fittings round the mast to quite elaborate structures. We built our main fife rail on the king plank, and for the mizzen we fitted belaying pins in the mast housing. If the mizzen is stepped through a bridge deck, fit a mast band fife rail.

Bending sails to spars in a gaff-rigged boat
If you have mast hoops they must be slipped over the mast before it is stepped. Otherwise you should use a lacing of 1 in. hemp. Lace the mainsail and mizzen to the gaff and boom with a long length of 2 lb. line and using separate lengths of line, make it fast at the throat and tack with several turns through an eyebolt on the spar; the peak and clew are fastened in the same way, but with a greater scope of line to act as an outhaul. The reason for the separate lengths of line, particularly at the outboard end of the boom and the gaff, is in the event of the long lines chafing through and parting. When bending new sails do not stretch them too tightly (just enough to take the wrinkles out of the canvas), and start with the throat, then the peak, then lace the head of the sail to the yard. Alternatively, instead of using one long lacing, you may use separate seizings for each eyelet.

The boom should be tackled in the same way but with a heavier line for the clew outhaul. The single foresail of a ketch is simple to set, as it is set flying, that is, it is not hanked onto a stay. The tack hooks onto the traveller on the bowsprit; the halyard shackles to the head, and the sheets, of course, to the clew. Haul out the foot, belay and hoist the sail. We belayed the outhaul to the bitts.

Leads of sheets and runners
This is best worked out by trial and error. The jib sheets may be led through thimbles on the fore shrouds, and then aft along the inside of the bulwark rail to be belayed on wooden cleats.

The jib, throat and peak halyards and the main topping lift will all belay to the fife rail.

Double main and mizzen sheets need little tending when under way; in tacking to windward the boom will swing over unattended.

The mizzen halyards lead to the fife rail. The mizzen sheets may lead to the horse and then to cleats on either side of the coaming, or alternatively to the horse, back to the boom end, along the boom to a block at the tack, and down to be belayed to the fife rail.

THREE

Engines and installations

The first thing in planning the engine installation for either a motor boat or an auxiliary sailing boat is to decide on the type of engine. For a motor boat between 14 ft and 40 ft waterline, a rule of thumb was to allow 1 h.p. for each foot of waterline length. A more realistic method is to check the h.p. of comparable craft in the plans published in the yachting press. Petrol engines, either new or second hand, are cheaper than marine diesel engines and they are lighter in weight, producing relatively more power per pound weight. Diesel engines are safer, much more economical to run and so more economical in space for fuel. They are also incomparably more reliable. Petrol engines depend on electrical systems to produce a spark; these systems are vulnerable to damp, a factor inherent in boating activities!

Diesel engines are not dependent on electrical systems and can practically run under water, providing the air intake is clear.

The ideal position for an engine in a boat is just abaft the midship section and on the centreline. For auxiliary sailing craft and for fishing boats that need a clear space amidships, the engine may have to be placed further aft. Most marine engine manufacturers will give the maximum angle for the stern shaft. This is usually not more than 12° off the horizontal.

Yacht designers have an awful habit of poking auxiliary engines into the most inaccessible corners of their often fine-lined craft. The converter of lifeboats, beach boats and fishing boats usually has more room to play with. Even so, it is most important that the engine should be completely accessible and this includes the stern gland. Ideally one should be able to walk round the engine or at least crawl round it. At the very least, one should be able to reach every part without difficulty and this includes the entire fuel line and the full length of the shaft. Fuel lines should have an adequate fall at any angle of heel. Exhaust pipes should be kept as short and as straight as possible. The fuel tank should have a filler cap above the deck and the tundish (funnel) should be long enough to reach down into the tank. Clean fuel is most important if an engine is to run properly, whether it is diesel or petrol. Water in petrol is all too common and is usually due to condensation. Incidentally, the time to fill up the fuel tank is at the end of a run, so that if there is any sediment in the tank it has time to settle before the next time the engine is run.

For air-cooled diesels, the layout must be carefully planned. It is particularly important that the hot air is ducted away and that there is an adequate supply of cool air. Proper ducts must be built to extract the hot air, but if the engine is not under a watertight cockpit, it can usually draw enough cool air from the bilges. It is, however, worth while ducting fresh air to the air intake.

Type of installation

The choice for single engined craft lies between a centreline shaft coming through the sternpost, and an offset shaft coming out of the stern of the boat but to one side of the sternpost. This method would be used in preference to a centreline installation in steel lifeboats. Finally, there is a quarter installation where the shaft needs external support.

There are advantages and disadvantages for both central (or offset) and quarter installations. The main difficulty with a central installation in a conversion is that the sternpost may not be wide enough to allow for

boring for the stern tube, and certainly will not be wide enough fore and
aft to allow for housing the propeller, so one has to cut a large aperture
out of the rudder, thus greatly impairing steering efficiency, or one has to
fit a false sternpost.

With the propeller on the centreline there is less drag when sailing,
particularly if you fit a two-bladed or feathering propeller. Also a centreline propeller does not get snarled up with mooring lines, etc. in the way
one in a quarter installation is liable to do. A three-bladed propeller has more
drag, but it is also much more efficient. For most conversions this more than
makes up for the very slight loss of speed under sail.

Centre installation
Having decided on the type of engine, make as accurate a sketch as you can
of the installation, showing the approximate position of the engine, the
position of the propeller and the line of the shaft. In an auxiliary installation
it is most important that you make sure there is enough width athwartships
to take engine bearers. These bearers should consist of two heavy floors
and two fore-and-aft members bolted over the floors, thus making a rigid
structure to which the steel bearers on the engine can be bolted.

In the case of an engine installation in a ship's lifeboat, a false keel or skeg
at least 4 in. to 6 in. deep is essential, in order to get the propeller deep
enough in the water, and also a false sternpost to house the propeller so that
no gap need be cut from the rudder.

Having worked out on the sketch the approximate angle of the propeller
shaft, offer up the propeller to the sternpost and mark the centre of its shaft
on the sternpost. The first job is to remove all the bolts that come in the way
of the shaft. These bolt holes must then be filled with hardwood plugs
which should either be glued into position or given a thick coating of white
lead paint just before inserting them. To avoid weakening it, it may well be
necessary to rebolt the sternpost assembly, drilling new bolt holes so that
they do not cut across the shaft line. Before the hole for the stern tube can
be bored, either the engine should be dropped into its approximate position
or a template of it offered up so that you can see the position and angle of
the shaft. Then drill a pilot hole with a $\frac{3}{4}$ in. bitt. The angle simply has to be
judged by eye. The inboard end of this hole will come through the stern
knee. One should have no difficulty in keeping it on a true centreline;
it is merely the angle from the horizontal that is difficult. When the pilot
hole is bored, take a piece of line through the hole and stretch it to the point
where the shaft coupling on the engine will come and fasten it somewhere

8 Baffle plates at stern to prevent
propeller cavitation

forward of where the engine would be (the engine is not yet aboard). Determine whether the angle is correct or too high or too low. If it is badly out in either direction, use a bull-nosed auger and correct the angle. The bull-nosed auger is an essential piece of equipment. The ordinary bitt will just follow the original direction of the hole, but the bull-nosed auger will enlarge the hole in any direction that you wish.

The stern tube for a 26 ft lifeboat installation will probably have an external diameter of about $1\frac{3}{4}$ in. As soon as the line of the pilot hole is correct, if you can, borrow from either the engine manufacturers or a shipwright a boring bar. The final hole will be bored from inside the boat, with jigs (blocks of wood with a hole in them) set up on the shaft line. The hole for the stern tube will be bored $\frac{1}{8}$ in. larger in diameter than the diameter of the stern tube. This is to allow for white lead packing compound, which is forced round the tube.

If the sternpost is too thin to take the stern tube, fit hardwood cheek pieces about $1\frac{1}{2}$ in. thick and about 2 ft long faired at top and bottom. The fitting of these cheek pieces where they abut the planks is not very easy, so it may be a simpler operation to take out the sternpost altogether and to fit a new, thicker and deeper fore-and-aft sternpost. The apron will hold the boat together. This removal of the sternpost is not nearly as difficult an operation as it sounds. As the hood ends will almost certainly have become somewhat frayed, it will make a neater job if the plank ends are sawn off flush with the apron and the new sternpost is fitted so that it overlaps the apron and covers the plank ends. This new sternpost should be made wide enough fore-and-aft to allow for the gap for the propeller. The bottom of the gap will be made up of a continuation of the false keel or skeg.

In any installation, the basic factors are a firm engine bed, a straight shaft and accurate alignment. The stern tube should be set in a shaft log which is an integral part of the ship. The propeller shaft must turn easily under hand pressure and show no hard spots (which are an indication of binding). The couplings must come together without being forced, and a feeler-gauge should show an even drag at any point between their faces, no matter how you rotate the engine and shaft. The beds on which the engine is set must be solid, and well built into the hull. The weight and working strains of the engine should be spread as much as possible. This can be done either by making the beds very long or by bolting them to heavy cross floors. The engine must be in perfect alignment with the propeller shaft, both vertically and horizontally, its exact position on the bed being adjusted by means of hardwood wedges or thin brass shims under its feet. Additional support for the shaft should be provided by plummer blocks. The rule of thumb for this is that not more than 40 diameters of the shaft should go unsupported. That is, if for example the shaft has a diameter of 1 in., then not more than 40 in. of shaft should be without support.

The alignment must be correct with the engine firmly bolted down and not just resting on the beds. Check all the bolts after a few hours' running.

This applies equally to engines set on flexible mountings. These are specially designed shock-absorbing feet, placed between the feet of the engine and the top of the beds. A flexibly mounted engine shows a good deal of movement when it is running with a load, but this is no excuse for neglecting its proper alignment at rest. The thrust of the propeller should be taken on a separate thrust block, and a short carden-shaft with universal joints used to connect the propeller shaft with the engine. This arrangement will work smoothly with the engine and the shaft several degrees out of line, but you must line up the engine properly, or the uneven strain will eventually force the engine and shaft out of line so much that the universal joints cannot transmit the power of the engine properly.

Universal joints together with an intermediate shaft are also very useful if, for some reason, the engine has to be slightly out of line with the propeller shaft, and they may enable you to install the engine in a more convenient position than might otherwise be possible. A single universal joint can be used if you are forced to put the engine at a slight angle to the propeller shaft; for example, if the shaft has to be at a steeper angle than is permissible for your particular engine.

Universal joints should not be confused with flexible couplings which may sometimes take their place, and will work quite well provided that the angle is small, and the power to be transmitted is low. But flexible couplings are really intended as safety measures in case the hull should work slightly under the strain of a rough sea or a heavy load. Neither flexible couplings nor universal joints should be expected to carry the thrust from the propeller, and a proper thrust bearing block should always be installed on the inboard end of the propeller shaft.

Wherever a single coupling or joint is used, it is very important that the shafts should be properly aligned. Remember that the drive is *angular*, and that therefore the centrelines of both shafts – driving and driven – should intersect on the exact centre of the coupling or the joint. Even with flexible couplings, *do not* line up the engine and shaft with the boat on land. The alignment is sure to alter when she is launched and the hull begins to take up in the water. The best order of working is as follows: align the engine and the shaft before launching, but do not bolt up the coupling; when the boat has been in the water for at least 24 hours, and has had time to take up, make the final alignment and bolt up the coupling; run the engine for three or four hours. If the boat can cruise about so much the better, but you can manage quite well by making her fast alongside, with plenty of fenders out and strong springs fore and aft. You should run the engine for roughly the same time in ahead and in astern, and keep a watch on the shaft gland. If it shows any sign of heating, stop the engine, uncouple the shaft, and see whether the alignment has changed. If it has, the engine must be re-aligned and the running test repeated.

When the pilot hole has been bored you can drive in the new fastenings for the keel, sternpost and deadwood. The new fastenings should be spaced at least twice their diameter from the old holes, and may come either side of them. Mark them in on your sketch and find the maximum length for the fastenings which will leave at least 1 in. of wood between them and the shaft hole. Some fastenings may have to come above the shaft, and be driven from inside the hull through the deadwood into the sternpost. If you can discover the moulding of the sternpost and the deadwood and transfer it to the sketch, it will make it much easier to find the correct length of the new fastenings. They may be large, galvanised coach screws the same size as, or a little larger than, the old bolts, or they may be drift bolts made by cutting the old bolts down to the right length. The drift bolts should end with a blunt taper for about $\frac{1}{2}$ in. in which the diameter is reduced by about a quarter. The holes should be $\frac{1}{16}$ in. narrower than the bolt, and between $\frac{1}{4}$ in. and $\frac{1}{2}$ in. longer. There is no difficulty in driving the coach screws, but boring their holes needs care. Measure the length of the unthreaded shank from the top of the head and bore a hole the same *diameter* as the shank to this depth. Then measure the diameter a quarter of the way up the thread from the point. Using a bit of this diameter continue the hole to its full depth, and remember that the heads of the keel bolts must be sunk flush. Finally, chisel out a hole to countersink the head with room enough all round to take a stout box spanner. Do not try to drive in drift bolts with a light hammer. They will go half way in and then stick and bend. Use a 5 lb. hammer for $\frac{1}{2}$ in. to $\frac{5}{8}$ in. bolts, and a 7 lb. or even heavier hammer for anything larger. Hit hard with deliberate blows, keep the hammer true and keep hammering. If you stop the bolt will stick.

In building a new boat, a shaft log would be incorporated in the sternpost assembly. It is very difficult to fit such a log in an old boat. A useful, simple and practical alternative is to fit a low bulkhead of $1\frac{1}{2}$ in. oak 18 in. forward of the sternpost. Clean down all woodwork aft of this bulkhead, make sure that it is completely dry and give it a coat of tar. Fit the stern tube but do not fasten up the end bearings. Grease the exposed tube and wrap it in brown paper and then fill the area between the bulkhead and the stern of the ship with either weak cement (6 parts sand to 1 part cement) or pitch. If cement is used it must be a weak mixture or it will crack. Pitch is better as it never hardens completely, but diesel fuel, petrol or paraffin can dissolve it.

A professional boatbuilder would always use a boring bar for opening up the shaft hole to its full size. For those unfamiliar with it, this tool is a long steel bar with a thread at one end and an adjustable cutter in the middle. The bar is held true with the shaft line by bearings at each end. One of the bearings is threaded, and as you turn the bar it screws through the hole. The cutter takes out a shaving each time until the hole is true to size. You are not likely to have a boring bar to hand, nor may you be able to borrow or wish to go to the trouble of making one just to bore one hole. A simple, if somewhat slow and dirty, method is to *burn* out the hole to the right size. All you need are several pieces of iron or steel bar about 6 in. long. Get your local smith to weld onto each of them a length of $\frac{1}{2}$ in. rod about 1 ft longer than the hole. The thicknesses of the bars should vary from a little larger than the pilot hole to $\frac{1}{8}$ in. less than the diameter of the stern tube, to allow for the charred wood in the final bore—or burn.

Mark out the edge of the finished hole on the after side of the sternpost, and cut this circle well into the wood with a narrow chisel. Taper the opening of the pilot hole, true to this circle, enough to let the smallest of your burning bars go in $\frac{1}{4}$ in. This will enable you to centre it in the excitement of trying to get the bar in before it cools. Heat the bar to a good red and force it into the pilot hole, keeping it as nearly in line with the hole as possible, and remembering in which direction, if any, the hole has to be 'drawn' on the inside. Keep on doing this until it has gone in an inch or two, and then take a sight through the hole. If you brush out the charred wood you should be able to see a shoulder where the two bores join, and you can judge whether the new bore is running true (or with the right deflection) by seeing whether the shoulder is the same size all the way round, or larger on one side than on the other. If the hole has to be 'drawn' across, pass the burning bar through several times, trying to force it in the right direction. Check the holes with a line and note if it is at all out of true. When the largest burning bar has been passed through the hole, clean out as much of the charred wood as you can, and try the stern tube for size. If it will not go in you must put the bar through again, working it backwards and forwards evenly over the whole bore. Check it for size again, and go on burning it out until the stern tube will just slide into the hole. If you are ready to fit the tube, clean the hole out thoroughly, and give it a good coat of white lead paint, and insert the tube before the paint has had time to set. Clean off the threads on the stern tube at once, and screw on the gland and the outer bearing. Make quite sure that these fittings bed down on their seatings without any forcing (which would throw them out of line and make the shaft bind). The makers usually supply or specify the fastenings to hold them in place.

Do not be tempted to use a long burning bar on the assumption that its length will keep it true. One tends to swing the end of a long bar in a circle, which results in a bell-mouthed hole, in which the stern tube will never seat truly. If one wants to draw a hole to one side at the far end, one has to force the bar in the opposite direction at the near end, with the result that the hole will be circular in the middle, but oval at each end.

The same method can also be used for offset and quarter installations, and for single or twin screws.

Offset installations

An offset shaft passes through the planking beside the sternpost. The shaft must be offset enough for the propeller blades to clear the sternpost by a distance of about $\frac{1}{6}$ of the diameter of the propeller; thus a 12 in. propeller should have the centre of its shaft offset 8 in. from the side of the sternpost.

Make a sketch to scale as before, except that the shaft line need not continue beyond the after side of the sternpost. The sketch will give you the distance from the bottom of the keel to the intersection of the shaft line and the after side of the sternpost. Measure this up on the boat and mark the point on the sternpost clearly. Take a short piece of, say, 1 in. × 6 in. plank with one true edge, and mark on it the distance between the side of the sternpost and the centre of the shaft line, leaving a few inches at each end. At the mark for the shaft line cut a shallow V, just deep enough to take the shank of your auger, with its centre level with the top edge of the board. Fasten the board to the after side of sternpost. The true top edge must be level with the mark on the sternpost, and the mark on the board must align with the edge of the sternpost. Use a spirit level to make sure that the board is level athwartships before finally fastening it in place. A diagonal brace will ensure that it remains rigid.

You must now find the point where the shaft line intersects the planking. If you have not a true set of the boat's lines this will be a matter of trial and error. Guess the rough position, and then plumb down at several points to the right measurements on a rule held square to the side of the keel. The line through these points will give the thwartship position of the shaft. To find its vertical position you will need someone to help you. First nail a straight-edged batten to the side of the keel; it should run from 1 ft aft of the stern-post to a little way forward of your rough position for the hole, and it should make the same angle with the bottom of the keel as the shaft line does in your sketch. Rest one end of a spirit level on the batten and drop a plumb line from the shaft height mark on the sternpost until the point of the bob just touches the level, while your thumbnail holds the line against the mark. Your assistant then moves the level forward keeping it true and hard down on the batten, while you run your thumbnail—still holding the same point on the plumb line—along the thwartship position line until the point of the bob just touches the level. This gives the position of the centre of the shaft hole. The point in the centre will be obliterated when you start boring, so you should scribe in reference marks at equal distances forward and aft and above and below it. The distance between each pair of marks does not matter, as they are only to indicate that the shaft line must come exactly in the centre.

Cut a seating for the point of the auger on the line of the shaft, set the auger in position, and carry on boring. When you are through the plank you can run a line to the strut inside the hull and find the position and shape for the shaft log. When you have cut the shaft log to shape, fit it in place and finish boring the hole.

Quarter installation
A quarter installation is arranged in the same way as an offset one, except that the shaft hole will probably be too far forward for the auger to rest on a strut attached to the sternpost. The strut, longer this time as the shaft will be further outboard, can be used as a base for the after end of a chalk line, the forward end of which is made fast to the hull at the same height as the centre of the shaft, and an inch or so outboard to give clearance for boring. The vertical position of the shaft hole can be found in the same way as before, but you will have to use a slightly different method of finding the thwartship position. The propeller is so far outboard that it will tend to force the boat's head in the opposite direction unless you counteract this thrust. A rule of thumb method is to mount the engine and shaft at such an angle that the shaft line, if produced, intersects the boat's centreline at the forward end of the waterline. If you have settled the thwartship position of the engine, and know the position of the coupling, it is easy to find the thwartship position of any point on the shaft line. Find the distance from the forward end of the waterline to the coupling and from the centreline to the centre of the coupling. It is then a matter of simple proportion. For instance: suppose the distance from the waterline at the bows to the coupling is 20 ft, and from the centreline to the coupling 5 ft; then centreline to shaft line at 40 ft is 10 ft, at 10 ft it is 2 ft 6 in. Attach a chalk line to the centre of the keel under the forward end of the waterline—or to a stake in the ground if the boat has overhang—and fasten the other end of the line near a line square off the sternpost and at a distance from the centreline calculated as described above.

By using this line as a datum, and plumbing down to it from the hull, you can mark a line on the planking. The shaft hole must come somewhere on this line, the exact point to be found with the help of the inclined batten and spirit level. You can then chop a small piece out of the planking to give a

square face to start the auger on, or, if the planking is at a very flat angle to
the shaft line, you can screw on a small wooden chock with a flat after face,
and start boring the hole through the chock. Once the hole is through
the planking, you can run a chalk line and find the exact shape and position
of the shaft log.

Shaft logs

The shaft logs in new boats are usually put in when the hull is built, and
then bored for the stern tube afterwards. In a conversion it is easier to make
the hole in the planking first, so that you can run an accurate line right
through the hull, thus making it much easier to measure the position of the
shaft and align it properly.

A shaft log for an offset and quarter installation is a stout hardwood chock
fitted to the inside of the planking to take the stern tube and inner gland
bearing. It must be firmly built into the hull, for any movement in the log
will affect the alignment of the tube and shaft. Keep this in mind when
fitting the log, but remember, too, that sheer weight of timber does not in
itself make for strength. Lighter scantlings, well fitted and properly
braced, will make a stronger job.

The length of the shaft log depends on the kind of installation—and there
are many. You can support the propeller with an outer log or 'blister'
instead of an A-bracket; alternatively you can use an A-bracket with a
short stern tube, the shaft being exposed between the tube and the bracket.
In either case you may be able to use a standard length of tube. The fore-
and-aft position of the after end of the stern tube is governed by that of the
propeller. Mark the position of the after flange on the chalk line and
measure off the length of the tube to the inside flange; then measure off the
radius of the flange, square off the chalk line towards the planking. If there
is room for the flange you need not carry the log any further forward, and
you can mark the position on the planking; but if there is not room for it
you will have to work forward along the line and mark the point where
there will be clearance between the flange and the planking. You must then
adjust the length of the tube accordingly.

If the stern tube is not to be carried to an A-bracket you will have to fit a
very small log on the outside of the planking, just large enough to take the
flange of the outer bearing, its size being found in the same way as for the
inside log. A 'blister' must extend far enough aft to bring the outboard
bearing close up to the propeller. The picture of the converted whaler on
page 117 shows a 'blister' support for a quarter installation. If the stern tube

runs right aft to an A-bracket you will only need an inside log.

When you know the position of the forward end of the log, you can make a template of thin wood, plywood, or stout card. It should be about 1 ft longer than the distance from the forward end of the log to the shaft hole, and wider than the distance between the planking and the chalk line. Cut one edge to fit the inside of the planking immediately under the line of the shaft, cutting it over any timbers that may be in the way. Put it in place and mark the shaft line on it. Then mark a second line on the template at a distance above the shaft line equal to twice the diameter of the stern tube: this line represents the top of the log, which should be at least three times as thick as the stern tube. You may have to cut some of the timbers to make room for the stern tube; but the timbers in the way of the log should be left intact, and the log cut to fit over them.

Lay your template on a piece of oak of the right thickness and mark off the lower edge. Cut the log to shape, leaving 1 in. to spare on the top. It should fit against the planking reasonably well if only along the line of the shaft, but it will probably still have to be cut to the shape of the section of the hull. Wedge the log in place and scribe a line all round it, so that you can take it out and be sure of putting it back in the same position. Then put a small flat block of $\frac{3}{4}$ in. timber on the planking beside the log. Lay a pencil hard down on the block and mark each side of the log by sliding the pencil and block along the planking.

Both sides are now marked off at an equal distance above the inside of the planking. If the log has to step over a land, mark both sides of the log where the log and the land intersect, and make a diagonal cut between these points. Cut the face of the log back to the lines you have just marked in, and try it in position again. It should be quite a good fit. Now rub a thick coat of chalk onto the planking under the log, put the log back in position and give it several light taps. You can then take it off and see where the chalk has marked it. Shave these spots down very carefully (it will be fairly clear to start with how much wood must come off). Carry on chalking and shaving until the log picks up a film of chalk over the whole surface. You can then cut the top to the right size and the log is all ready to go in.

Give the planking and the face of the log a good coat of thick lead paint – the thicker the better. Put the log in position and fasten it temporarily with a couple of screws driven up through the planking. Now scribe two lines down the top of the log, about $\frac{3}{4}$ in. from each edge, and set out on them the position of the bolts, which should be spaced 3 or 4 in. apart, and kept clear of the timbers. Bolts of $\frac{3}{8}$ in. are suitable for engines up to 8 h.p. and $\frac{1}{2}$ in.

bolts for larger ones. Drill for two bolts at each end of the log, put them in and do the nuts up hand tight before doing the same with the rest of the bolts. Do not forget to put a washer under each nut. When all the bolts are in, go round with a spanner and give each nut a full turn. Work in pairs until they are all tightened up to an even pull on the spanner and the paint squeezes out of the joint. Leave it for a few hours and then tighten up again.

If there is a blister or an outer log it should be fitted before you bolt up the shaft log inside, for the two logs will overlap, and some of the bolts will go right through both of them. The bolts should either have convex heads or be countersunk, and should be driven from outside the boat. Galvanised coach bolts are quite suitable; the square section just below the head prevents the bolt from turning with the nut, and this is a great help if you are working single handed.

Split shaft logs
These are made in two pieces and joined along the line of the centre of the shaft. Thus you can make the hole for the stern tube half in each section, before the log is fitted. Make the lower half of the log in the usual way, but with the top face only as high as the line of the centre of the shaft. Then make another block of the same width and twice as thick as the diameter of the stern tube. The upper piece fits onto the lower one, and its after end fits onto the planking. Mark the shaft line on the lower piece of the log, take them both out of the boat, and gouge a half-round trough out of each piece so that they fit the stern tube exactly. Clamp the log together with the tube in place, and check that the joint comes dead in the centre of the tube, and that the two parts fit snugly against one another. Fasten the split log into the boat just as if it were a solid one. Split logs can also be used outside the hull, and provide a simple way of making blisters.

It may be necessary to strengthen the hull round the shaft log, to prevent it from working and throwing the shaft out of alignment. The log for an offset shaft is usually low enough in the boat for you to put a deep wooden floor right across the hull and over the log; and this will give you all the stiffening you need. A long log should have two floors across it. But in a quarter installation it is unlikely that you will be able to put a floor so high up inside the hull without it getting in the way. The best method in this case is to fit forged strap-iron clamps to each timber in the way of the shaft log. They run over the log, and for about 1 ft along the timber on each side of it. They should be at least 1 in. $\times \frac{3}{8}$ in. in section, and be clench-fastened through the timbers. Arrange the bolts for the log so that two go through each strap.

Galvanise the straps if possible, or, failing this, heat them and dip into tar.

If you are having an A-bracket it is well worth trying to use a standard fitting supplied by the makers of the engine. Send them the details of the bracket you want, the vertical and horizontal angles between the shaft line and the hull at the point where the bracket is to be fitted, and also the distance between the line and this point, and ask what is the nearest that they can supply. If their bracket only differs slightly from yours, you may be able to adjust the shaft line to suit it. If you cannot get a standard bracket to fit, you will have to make a pattern and have it cast and bored to take the bearing. Each leg of the bracket should have a large foot fastened to the hull by at least two bolts. The bracket puts a good deal of strain on the hull. It should, if possible, come between two timbers; and the hull should be strengthened inside with a pad of wood between the timbers. This pad should be at least 6 in. wide and come flush with the inside of the timbers. Make another pad, similar to the first but slightly longer so as to span the adjacent pair of timbers. Paint the whole thing thoroughly and clench-fasten it through the planking and the timbers, leaving plenty of room for the bracket bolts. Sometimes you can simplify an offset installation by fastening the bracket to the side of the sternpost or to the deadwood.

Engine beds

Oak, wych elm, Canadian rock elm, and pitch pine are all suitable for engine beds; so is Douglas fir, which is moreover particularly easy to work.

With the stern tube in position, the engine bearers can now be built; the floors should be not less than 3 in. thick and the fore-and-aft members the same thickness, and joggled over the floors and through-bolted or fastened down with heavy coach screws. The engine bed should be at least $\frac{1}{4}$ in. lower than the estimated position for the base of the engine. The lining up is completed with the use of metal shims. The engine and stern tubes should first of all be lined up when the boat is on land and finally coupled up when the boat is afloat.

Fore-and-aft beds should be at least three times as long as the distance between the engine bolts. The engine bolts should come on the fore-and-aft centreline of each bed. The installation drawing supplied by the maker of your engine will give the distance athwartships between the centres of the bolts.

The height from the top of the engine beds to the shaft line varies from engine to engine; you can find it from the maker's installation diagram. Adjust your measurements accordingly, but it is a good plan to leave the top edge of the beds a little too high until just before they are fastened to the hull, and then plane them down to the right level, i.e. $\frac{1}{4}$ in. lower than the proper height, to allow for metal shims.

Before fastening the beds in position the top edges should be trued up. Use the distance from the shaft line given by the engine makers, *plus* $\frac{1}{16}$ in. if the engine feet are *below* the shaft line, and *minus* $\frac{1}{16}$ in. if they are *above*. If the engine is to be held down by coach *screws* you can go ahead and fasten the beds. If bolts are to be used, proceed as follows: true up the top edge of the beds parallel to the shaft line, and level athwartships. Find the fore-and-aft position of the engine bolts by measuring the distance from the propeller to the coupling, and from the coupling to the bolts. Mark the bolt positions on the tops of the beds. Then take the beds out of the boat and mark lines square across the top of each bed and down one side. Measure down the side a distance equal to the length of the bolts less the depth of the feet and nuts. This will mark the top of the slot which must be cut through the beds to take the nuts on the bolts. These slots should be about $\frac{1}{8}$ in. deeper than the thickness of the nuts, and wide enough to take a spanner.

The beds are now ready for fixing. Use bolts, if possible: $\frac{3}{8}$ in. galvanised coach bolts are suitable for most boats. They should be spaced about 6 in. apart. Unusually large or powerful engines will, of course, need heavier mountings. If you cannot use bolts for all the fastenings of the beds, 14 or 16 gauge screws should be driven up through the planking, and should go at least 3 in. into the bed. Screws must be spaced more closely than bolts, *not more* than 6 in. apart. But try to have a bolt at each end of the beds, and at least one under the engine.

If the beds are not more than about 9 in. high there is no need to brace them. But if they are higher, you should put in knees and perhaps some additional bracing between them. Simple bracings can be made of deep pieces of timber $\frac{7}{8}$–1 in. thick, with the grain running horizontally between the beds. Make them, and mark their exact position, before the beds are finally fastened. Screw fillets of 1–1$\frac{1}{2}$ in. timber to the insides of the beds when you give them their final truing up. The braces can then be screwed to the fillets when the beds are in place. Knees can be fastened to the beds in the same way, their other arms being screwed to the planking from outside, or clenched. There should be a bracing just forward and just aft of the engine; there should also be knees if the beds are very high. An offset or quarter installation will probably need knees only for the inboard bed.

Another way of bracing is to run a strap of mild steel bar from a timber across the tops of the beds and down to the same timber again. This strap should be fastened to the beds with coach screws. Its ends, which must be bent to follow the timber, should be bolted or clenched right through.

Fitting the stern tube

The stern tube can now be fitted. Paint it, preferably with white lead, and work plenty of paint into the shaft hole. Take off the inboard gland and slide the tube gently into position. Wipe off any paint that has got onto the thread and carefully screw the gland back on. Check that the flanges on both fittings bed down properly onto their seatings. Slacken the fittings and put plenty of white lead under them. Tighten them up again and fasten them with screws. See that the grease cup on the inboard gland is in an accessible position, for it will need regular attention.

Make sure that there is no dirt or grit in the stern tube bearings, wipe the propeller shaft clean, and slide it into place. Fit the propeller, but do not tighten it up yet. There is usually a clearance of $\frac{1}{16}$ in. to $\frac{1}{8}$ in. between the propeller and the nearest bearing, so take a piece of plywood or cardboard of the right thickness, cut a slot in it, and fit it over the shaft between the propeller and the bearing. You can then pull the shaft up hard from inside the boat, and be sure of having the right clearance. Fit the coupling and its key in place on the shaft, and fasten them tightly. Make the engine drip-tray, and install it.

Aligning the engine

You can then get the engine on board. Set it on its bed and work it aft until the couplings touch. Bring the couplings together and note in which direction the engine must be moved to bring them into line. The beds should have been arranged so that the engine has to be lifted slightly. This is done by putting shims of thin brass under the engine feet. Work the engine in the right direction, raising or lowering it by means of the shims, until the spigot on one part of the coupling enters the recess in the other. Then bring the faces of the couplings as close together as possible. You will probably find that the flanges meet on one side only, and there is a gap on the other side. The secret of aligning an engine is to make the flanges meet exactly, and it is worth any amount of trouble to ensure that they do. Ease the forward end of the engine one way or the other. Move it up or down by adding or removing shims from under the engine feet. Disconnect the coupling frequently to make sure that the spigot is not binding in its socket and springing the shaft.

When the coupling fits fairly well you can start on the final alignment. You will need a feeler gauge. It consists of several thin strips of steel, their thicknesses graduated in thousandths of an inch. Wipe the faces of both flanges quite clean, bring them together, and insert a 3 or 4 thousandth feeler gauge. Draw it gently round the coupling, noting where there is a drag and where the feeler is slack. The forward end of the engine must be moved very slightly towards the side that is slack. Try again with the feeler until there is an even drag all round the coupling, and the feeler is gripped at any point round the coupling if you apply a slight pressure to the propeller shaft. Mark round the engine feet with a fine, sharp pencil as a check in case there is any movement, and bore for the bolts. Put them in and tighten them up. Check the coupling again. You will probably find that the alignment has altered, and the engine has drawn down either bodily or at an angle. If so, you will have to add some more shims. Tighten up the bolts and check again. This somewhat trying business goes on until the coupling is properly aligned.

Bolt up the coupling, put the engine in neutral, and turn the propeller. You should be able to spin it with one finger on the tip of the blade, and without feeling any point at which it drags or becomes stiff. Break the coupling and withdraw the coupling spigot. Your engine should now be as well aligned as it is possible to get it on shore, but make sure that you check it, and if necessary correct it, after your boat is launched. Do not forget what I said at the beginning of this chapter about running-in.

Tanks and pipes

The tanks and their pipes can now be put in. They vary so much with the boat and the type of engine that I can only give general instructions, but two rules hold good in every case: keep the fuel tanks and their pipes well away from the exhaust; and if any part of the exhaust system is likely to become hot, keep it well clear of the woodwork, and cover it thoroughly with asbestos putty or string.

Fuel tanks should be of copper for petrol and mild steel for diesel. The use of these different metals for the tank is important. The fuel lines, however, for both petrol and diesel can be of copper. Linings of Epikote resins have been proved satisfactory for all fuels. If your tanks are specially made for you, they should be of all-welded construction. To take up vibration or any other movement, three horizontal circular turns should be made in the fuel line near the engine. It is advisable to incorporate at least one filter in the line. After some years of use, copper fuel lines can become brittle.

This can be remedied by taking the lines out of the boat, heating them and annealing them. They can then be replaced. On no account use plastic fuel lines. In the case of fire these melt, and one is then really in trouble.

Fuel tanks should be placed well away from the engine and as high as possible, so as to give a good gravity feed. If they are suspended under the deck you will need good solid chocks over the tank, and brass or copper straps underneath it. Pad the chocks and the straps with felt. Fuel pipes must have a gentle fall over their whole length. Even the shortest upward slope tends to cause air-locks. Clip the pipe to solid supports (timbers or the bulkhead framing), and put at least one complete turn in the pipe at some point near the engine to allow for expansion and contraction. There should be a cock at each end of the pipe; make sure that they are easy to get at. The fuel tank should have a filter built into it, but put in another near the engine. Fuel has a lot of dirt in it these days.

Exhaust systems may be either wet or dry. In a wet system some of the water that cools the engine is diverted into the silencer, thus cooling the silencer and the tail pipe, and cutting down the noise of the exhaust. In a dry system all the water from the engine goes overboard by a separate pipe, and the exhaust is hot and dry all the way along. The wet system is far the better. It is installed as follows.

The engine makers usually give details of the ideal exhaust installation. Following their advice, and remembering that bends in the exhaust should be as easy as possible, choose a position for the silencer well above the waterline and with the after end about $\frac{1}{2}$ in. lower than the forward end. Clamp the silencer temporarily in position, and bend a piece of $\frac{1}{4}$ in. rod to the shape of the pipe between the engine and the silencer. Decide where the exhaust outlet should pass through the hull—it should be a good deal lower than the silencer—and bend another piece of rod to the shape of the tail pipe. Take both rods along with the actual exhaust pipe to a boatbuilding or engineering works, and get them to bend the pipes on a proper pipe-bender. One can do the bending oneself, by filling the pipes with pitch, and heaving them round some firm object, but the result is usually anything but sightly. While the pipes are being bent, get the boatyard to braze a bush into the lowest point of the engine pipe, and have it threaded to take a small drain-cock. If there are flanges they can be brazed on at the same time.

When the pipes come back, bent to shape, try them against the engine and silencer. You may have to move the silencer a little in order to tighten up the union nuts or flanges. Make two strip-metal brackets to hold the silencer securely in place, leaving enough room for a strip of asbestos between it and the bracket. The engine pipe will become fairly hot, so serve it with two thicknesses of asbestos string, and put a guard over any part of the pipe that is exposed to the cockpit or the inside of a locker.

The exhaust cooling water pipe can now be run. It leads from a union on the engine to another on the silencer. It will be quite a small pipe, and can be bent by hand to follow the engine pipe. The cooling water tell-tale which shows that the engine cooling water is circulating properly is a small pipe leading from a union on the engine to a skin fitting outlet, which should be so placed that you can easily see the stream of water flowing out of it.

The cooling water intake has still to be fitted. Its skin fitting should be as near the keel as possible so that it is always well under water however much the boat rolls and pitches; but it should also be easily accessible, for the cock will have to be turned off every time you finish with the engine. The makers will provide a filter for the water intake; it goes outside the planking and should have the open end forward in order to scoop up as much water as possible. If you are going to cruise on weedy rivers it is a good plan to fit a combined sea cock and filter inside the boat so that you can clean it out while the boat is afloat. The top of the filter must not be below the waterline.

When you are choosing where to put the water intake, consider whether the boat is ever likely to dry out on soft mud. If she is, you must find a place for the intake where it will not be choked with mud when she grounds.

There are three kinds of pipe joints: firstly, union and nut, consisting of a cone-ended sleeve that fits over the end of one pipe, and carries a nut which screws onto a thread on another sleeve (with an internal cone) which fits on the second pipe. The second fitting may be part of the engine or some other fixture to which the pipe is attached. One can buy reducing sockets for joining pipes of different sizes. The unions should be joined to the pipes with silver solder, for soft solder is likely to melt should the engine catch fire. If the joint of a fuel pipe melted in a fire the results would be as disastrous as if the fuel line was of plastic.

The second kind of union consists only of a nut and a small sleeve, called an onion, which fits over the end of the pipe. The nut is slipped over the end of the pipe, followed by the onion, and the nut is then screwed up tight onto the fitting. Screwing up the nut squeezes the onion onto the pipe and the seating, resulting in a very tight joint.

The third method is usually reserved for exhaust and other fairly large pipes. A hollow nut screws onto the fitting on the engine; it has a hole slightly larger than the pipe. Soften the end of the pipe, making sure that it is square. Slip the nut over it and, with a light ball-ended hammer, gently bell the end of pipe outwards for about $\frac{1}{8}$ in. until it will just fit into the hollow of the nut. When you tighten up the nut it presses the end of the pipe firmly onto its seating. Instead of belling out the end of the pipe, you may silver-solder a bronze ring onto it at about $\frac{1}{4}$ in. from the end.

Air ducts for diesels
Air-cooled diesels have their cooling air drawn in by a fan embodied in the flywheel. This directs the air over the cylinder, but for the cooling to be efficient the air supply must consist of cold air and have an unrestricted flow. Likewise, the hot air must be properly led away so that it cannot re-circulate.

It is most important to make your air ducts to the dimensions recommended by the makers. If you make the area of the cross section too small, your engine will heat up and lose power. You must avoid sharp bends in the ducting, for a right-angled bend can increase resistance to the airflow by 80 *per cent*. No bends should be of a radius of less than five times that of the trunking. This air ducting is by no means a waste of space in a conversion for it can be used for heating the cupboard in which you dry your oilskins or other damp clothes. It can be constructed of flexible tube supplied by the engine makers or it can be made of canvas or plywood. If you are in any doubt, ask the manufacturers. Even if your engine is in an open cockpit with a wooden cover, take care to see that the flow of air is adequate.

Electric system
If your engine has a starting handle you must allow plenty of room to swing it. If you have an electric starter follow the engine maker's wiring diagram carefully. The leads from the battery to the engine must have their terminal lugs soldered on, and be supported well clear of water from the bilge. Make a strong box with a lid to house the batteries; line it with lead if possible, otherwise coat the inside with hot paraffin wax. Mount the box on strong bearers in an accessible position, so that you can inspect the batteries, and top them up with distilled water. The bottom of the box should project about $1\frac{1}{2}$ in. to make a flange by which the box can be fastened down. Put the starter switch in a protected but accessible position. Remote control switches are usually incorporated in the instrument panel. The leads for the ammeter and voltmeter should be as short as possible and be neatly clipped to the bulkhead or to some other firm support. There is usually an oil pressure gauge; its pipe should follow the other leads to the instrument panel.

It is worth taking great pains in installing your engine. It may save your life in an emergency. Finally, it is no use taking care in the installation of the engine and its gear if you immediately forget about the whole thing, and leave it damp and uncared for until it breaks down. Use a spanner regularly on loose nuts to ensure a sound engine; clean the filters regularly and it will help ensure trouble-free running. Two-strokes need plenty of clean spare plugs and the minimum of slow running, if you are to rely on them to get you home. For water cooled engines, watch their water pumps and have spare neoprene vanes to hand for Jabsco pumps. Most marine engine manufacturers use these admirable pumps, which need no priming. The neoprene vane is the only part that can wear. To change the vane only takes about five minutes.

Air-cooled diesels must have the hot air ducted away and cold air ducted to them, otherwise they will heat and finally seize up. Unless an auxiliary engine is completely reliable it is better to have nothing to do with one. For the converter of fishing boats and other fairly heavy craft, air-cooled diesels, with their economy of running, ease of starting, lack of water pumps, and general reliability and ruggedness have great advantages. There are no electrics to go wrong, no water systems to jam up the pumps or to freeze up in winter, and no danger from fire from petrol fumes. Against this, they are noisier than water cooled diesels. This noise factor can be mitigated by lagging the engine box with glassfibre. Such noise as there is is a small price to pay for reliability.

For small craft the two-stroke petrol engine, which is a mechanically simple and relatively inexpensive engine, is better than a four-stroke engine at producing power at the right speed, so that reduction gears are not necessary and a direct drive propeller can make efficient use of this power to push the boat along. Also, two-stroke engines are more compact than most four-strokes. These advantages more than make up for their slightly more extravagant fuel consumption in terms of pints-per-brake-horse-power-per-hour. The commonest make of 8 h.p. two-stroke (Stuart Turner) will run for one and a half hours on a gallon of fuel. A single-cylinder 4 h.p. engine will run twice as long for the same amount of fuel. A point in favour of the two-stroke is that it revels in running long hours continually at full throttle. Hence their wide use for generating plants. But they don't like idling. The petrol and oil mixture on which they run is designed for a full load performance. When they idle they oil up and stop and nothing will persuade them to start again unless you carry a supply of clean plugs. Even then, if they are hot, they can show a reluctance to start again.

The four-stroke OHV petrol engine, the common car engine, hardly needs describing here. Many of the marine four-strokes are based on automobile units converted for marine purposes. There is more than one make based on the 10 h.p. Ford engine. They do not oil up like two-strokes, but mechanically they are more complicated and so have more things to go wrong. Thus a four-stroke engine needs frequent attention, especially if it has electric starting. The batteries must be properly looked after and kept fully charged. If the engine is neglected the valves are liable to rust up, or at least to stick. The lubricating oil in the sump needs frequent changing, and so on.

Air-cooled diesels
The disadvantages of air-cooled diesels are the noise, and the space that their air trunking occupies. As I mentioned above, noise can be lessened by lagging with glassfibre. This is not so much a matter of enclosing the noise as of absorbing it. The glassfibre must be in the form of a resin-bonded mat of about 1 in. thickness. Any smell of diesel oil can be greatly reduced by introducing an additive to the fuel such as Redex Diesel Deodorant.

Small diesel marine engines
The following propulsion units are all four-stroke diesel engines. Modifications and changes in their production may render these particulars obsolete, but at least this is an indication of the type of engine suitable for various kinds of conversion. Of these engines (up to 16 h.p.) two are Scandinavian in origin and two are British.

Volvo Penta MD1 7 h.p. one-cylinder four-stroke is an exceptionally compact little engine, 620 mm (24 in.) long by 395 mm (16 in.) wide and 640 mm ($25\frac{1}{4}$ in.) high. It is a water cooled unit, with 2:1 reduction gear, and weighs 130 kilos (285 lbs). The fuel consumption is only about 1 litre per hour. The MD1 would be ideal as an auxiliary in any conversion up to 26 ft overall. The maximum inclination for installation is 15°. In the same range the two-cylinder version rates 16·5 h.p. These engines are manufactured by A.B. Volvo Penta, Göteborg, Sweden.

Petter Marine Diesel AB1 WM 5 h.p. one-cylinder four-stroke is a compact little engine 784 mm ($30\frac{7}{8}$ in.) long by 527 mm ($20\frac{3}{4}$ in.) wide and 581 mm ($22\frac{7}{8}$ in.) high. It is a water cooled unit with a 2:1 reduction gear and weighs 84 kilos (185 lbs). It develops 5 b.h.p. at 3000 r.p.m. The maximum inclination for installation is 22° and the drive is for a right-handed propeller. The engine is fitted with forward/reverse gear and with either a 2:1 or 3:1 reduction drive. Raised hand starting is fitted at the forward end. Stern gear, exhaust system, etc. can be supplied as extras. The engine is one of a wide range of marine engines manufactured by Petters Ltd, Hamble, Southampton, England.

Saab Diesels Models H and HG. 6–8 h.p. one-cylinder four-stroke engines can be supplied either (Model H) with reversible mechanism clutch and the Sabb variable pitch propeller, diameter 394 mm (15$\frac{1}{2}$ in.), or (Model HG) with reverse gearbox and three-blade fixed propeller, diameter 380 mm (15 in. by 12 in.). It is rated at 6 h.p. at 1500 r.p.m. a maximum 8 h.p. at 2000 r.p.m. It is a water cooled unit with 2:1 reduction gear. The engine is approx. 685 mm (27 in.) in length by 450 mm (17$\frac{3}{4}$ in.) wide and 685 mm (27 in.) high and weighs 165 kilos (364 lbs). Each engine is supplied with complete equipment for installation in a boat, including stern gear, cooling water pump, rear start, silencer, exhaust pipe, stern greaser, foundation bolts, sea cock, fuel tank, tubing, tool kit with tools, gaskets, spares and instruction book. This engine would be suitable for power conversions up to 24 ft or as an auxiliary for heavier craft. There are also single-cylinder Sabb Diesel engines rated at 10 b.h.p., 16 b.h.p. and 20 b.h.p.

Lister Diesel air-cooled engines have been used for many years for industrial purposes. These extremely rugged, virtually trouble-free engines make ideal propulsion units for conversion where saving of weight and size is not important. Air-cooled diesel engines are particularly useful for inland waterway and canal use, where only too often the water pumps get choked up with mud, etc. I speak enthusiastically about these engines, for I have used one for the last ten years. Never once has it faltered or let me down. The Lister SRMG/R range are four-stroke, vertical, compression ignition units built as one-, two- and three-cylinder engines developing 6·5 h.p. per cylinder at 2000 r.p.m. and supplied with or without reduction gear (2:1).

The makers state that the one-cylinder engine has inherent out-of-balance forces which increase with engine speed. This can cause vibration if installed in lightly constructed craft. For most purposes for solidly built craft up to 26 ft overall the 13 b.h.p. two-cylinder Lister air-cooled diesel is a very satisfactory solution. The dimensions are 999 mm (39$\frac{3}{8}$ in.) long by 635 mm (25 in.) wide and 741 mm (29$\frac{1}{4}$ in.) high.

The weight of the two-cylinder engine with reduction gear is 300 kilos (663 lbs). Electric starting, dynamo, etc. and stern gear, exhaust system, fuel tanks, flexible hose for air trunking, etc. can be supplied as optional extras.

Listers have now developed water cooled units from the one- and two-cylinder engines. These engines are slightly quieter and develop rather more b.h.p. The two-cylinder has a continuous rating of 15 b.h.p. at 2000 r.p.m. with a maximum rating of 21 b.h.p. at 2000 r.p.m. This engine weighs 276 kilos (610 lbs). Lister diesel engines are manufactured by Lister Blackstone Mirrlees Marine, Dursley, Gloucester.

When more power is needed for heavy craft, such as converted fishing boats, there is an embarrassingly wide choice of diesel engines, many of them based on engines used in trucks, agricultural tractors, buses, etc.

The Newage range is based on the British Motor Corporation's engines, the Parsons diesels are based on Ford units, and so on. At the top end of the price range are the Gardner Marine Diesel units which are designed for heavy duty commercial craft as well as fishing boats, RNLI lifeboats and power cruisers. These are the Rolls-Royces of marine engines. Most converters will probably have to be content with less refined machinery, unless they are fortunate enough to be able to pick up one of these engines second hand. The installation of these and other equally complicated pieces of machinery is quite outside the scope of this book.

FOUR

Miscellaneous small conversions

Nearly every coastal village in Britain had its particular craft for inshore fishing, shaped over the years according to local needs. On the north-east coast of England from the Tweed to the Farne Islands there were two basic types of craft in use. The first of these was the double-ended type, i.e. they were sharp sterned and were locally called keel boats. They were good seaworthy craft, setting a tall lugsail on a single mast. The second type was the coble. These were widely used, particularly from the Farne Islands southwards to the Humber. The coble is a very idiosyncratic craft, with a sharp, high-bowed stem and a flat-bottomed stern. They were developed to be launched off shingle beaches. These craft, lugsail rigged, were from 25 ft to 27 ft overall. They are ideal for their proper purpose, and though cobles have been converted and decked in, I cannot think that they would offer very much in the way of conversion for auxiliary sailing and cruising boats. Used with an awning, they would make perfect camping boats.

A Yorkshire coble was sailed and rowed in 1961 by John Seymour from Scarborough to Brightlingsea. These curious craft, with their flaring bows and flat shallow sterns, are peculiarly suited to the East Coast. The shingle banks of this coast are not the cosiest places to land, but a coble, properly handled, is as nearly perfect for this purpose as can be. They are brought through the surf stern first, and the long flat stern is run up on the beach whilst the high bows should under normal conditions keep the breakers out. The crew jumps overboard and hauls the boat clear of the water. Like any beach boat they should be fitted with a steel-plated skeg with a hole through it, so that if a winch is available, the boat can be hauled up on the beach. A plate with a similar hole should be fitted at the foot of the stem for hauling off the beach.

The full-bodied beach boats from further down the East Coast, such as the Sheringham crabbers or the Aldeburgh boats, are a much better proposition for conversion. I know of one double-ended Sheringham boat that was most successfully converted into an auxiliary cutter. She was about 20 ft overall and was a most able little craft. Her freeboard had been raised by one strake and the forepart decked over to make a cabin. Her keel had been deepened by the addition of a 9 in. false keel. Her ballast was carried inside. Her cabin only had sitting headroom but she was used for many years on the river Stour for pleasure sailing, for fishing and even for wildfowling. She was a robust little boat, clinker-built and with a good deal more character to her than most converted lifeboats possess. The first time she was ever used for wildfowling was on a bitter frosty night in February. The wildfowlers from Manningtree used to paddle about five miles down the river on the tide to Holbrook Bay where in hard weather as many as 10,000 widgeon may be resting on the water. These punt gunners would lie up on the edge of the saltings waiting for first light. On this occasion the owner of the Sheringham boat had sailed down to Holbrook Bay on the previous evening, towing his punt with him. Whilst his fellow punt gunners were slowly freezing solid in their frail craft, he was lying comfortably abed with a glowing hot stove to keep him company. Just before first light, he roused himself, put on plenty of warm clothes and came on deck. He pulled the punt up alongside and carefully climbed down into it. What he had not allowed for was that the floorboards of the punt would be covered in ice. His feet went from under him and he fell backwards into the bottom of the punt, which sheered off from the parent craft. One of his feet got mixed up with the lines which held the little short paddles, and they in turn got muddled up with the punt gun. The next thing was a resounding explosion. Ten thousand ducks took off for the open sea. The punt gun (with no safety catch on) had gone off and blown a hole as big as a football right on the waterline of his fishing boat. He managed to beach her just before she sank. No one got any ducks that morning. He frapped a sail over the hole, baled her out and sailed off, back to Manningtree.

The repair of such a hole in a clinker-built craft is not difficult. The procedure is to cut away the broken planks so that the places where the new pieces are fitted do not come at the same point (see page 131). It is better to double up the new timbers, rather than to try and scarph in new pieces. The scarph in the planks should not be less than 4 in. long and should not end in a feather edge. Before finally fitting and fastening the surfaces of the scarph they should be well coated with white lead paint and fitted while the paint is still wet.

The beach boats on the Sussex coast are of a very old type. The Brighton hoggies are typical of these apple-bowed, broad-beamed, clinker-built craft. They were strongly built, with heavy sawn timbers and bilge keels to take some of the wear from the shingle beaches. They sit bolt upright on these keels. Their original rig was a single mast with a spritsail. The few that are left would make very roomy conversions and no doubt very slow sailers.

There are various other small craft on the South Coast. A pretty little model to be found on the Solent is the Itchen Ferry punt, in size anything from 19 ft to 25 ft overall, with a beam of about 8 ft 3 in. and a draught of 3 ft 6 in. They were cutter rigged with a pole mast and a topsail on a yard that stuck up above the masthead by 4 ft or 5 ft. They were used for shimping and inshore fishing. E. J. March, writing of the Itchen Ferry boats, said: "The boats are smartly kept, mast and spars nearly always varnished, with a touch of white at the end of the boom and bowsprit; topsides grey, white or blue with a black top strake, bottom red, black or dark green. Name and registry numbers in black or white according to the colour of the top strake."*

The little Itchen Ferry shrimper called the *Nellie*, which was built by Dan Hatcher in 1862, is still afloat on Southampton Water. W. M. Blake took her lines in the summer of 1932. *Nellie* had been in the ownership of

Inshore Craft of Great Britain Vol II, Edgar J. March, David & Charles, Newton Abbot, 1970

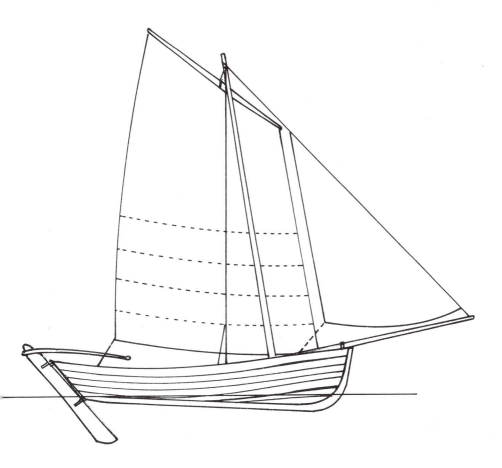

Fig. 23 Yorkshire coble 25 ft 6 in. overall

the same family for many years. She had been well cared for and carried 25 hundredweight of iron ballast.

Boats of this type, three-quarter decked, would be a simple proposition for conversion. In the case of a boat as old as *Nellie* it would, I think, be more rewarding to restore her to her original condition.

Down in the West Country, small inshore fishing boats such as the Mevagissy toshers (20 ft) are used for line fishing for mackerel during the spring and summer. These boats, which began as half-decked designs

Fig. 24 Sheringham crab boat 18 ft 6 in.
overall

after the 1914–18 war, were later decked in with just two large midships
wells – one for the nets, the other for the fish. Their two-masted rig carried
lugsails on both masts. The use of a mizzen mast in these fishing boats has
had remarkable persistance and has overlapped the age of power. For
instance, in the Aldeburgh boats, it is only since they have taken to the use
of air-cooled Lister diesels that the use of the mizzen sail has finally been
dropped.

Many of the Mevagissey toshers were built by Percy Mitchell in the
neighbouring hamlet of Port Mellon.* The toshers (or tossers) were carvel-
built with an oak backbone, steamed Canadian rock elm timbers and fir

*For anyone interested in these little fishing boats, or in the craft of boat building. *A Boat
Builder's Story* by Percy Mitchell, published in Mevagissey, is informative and interesting

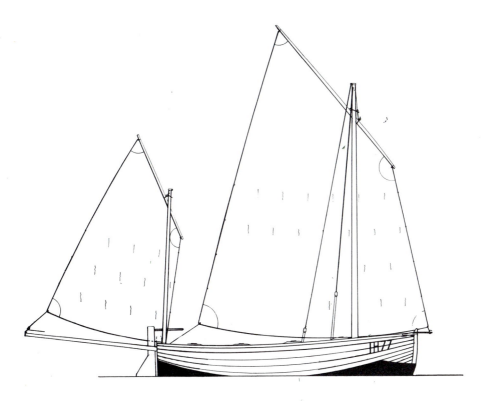

Fig. 25 Aldeburgh beach boat 16 ft
overall

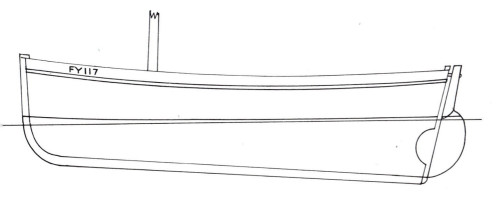

Fig. 26 Mevagissey tosher 20 ft overall

planking. They have a short deck forward and also at the stern. The only caulking is where the garboards meet the keel. All the other seams in the boat take up after it has been in the water for a short while. The toshers were very well built and at all important joints where stem or stern meet the keel stopwaters were fitted. The stopwater in a tosher is a $\frac{5}{8}$ in. softwood plug driven into a hole which is bored through the side of the keel at the level of the garboard rabbet wherever there may be a joint. The plug swells when it is wet and stops any water seeping up the joint.

The toshers are sturdy little craft and would make useful little motor-sailing cruisers. They have a reasonable moulded depth so only the minimum of building up would be necessary to provide a little cabin forward. The toshers were originally fitted with a 3 h.p. Kelvin engine. I would think that for cruising purposes a 6–8 h.p. diesel, either air-cooled or water cooled, would make a better propulsion unit.

Camping cruisers
Cruising in an open boat conjures up a rather Spartan way of life. It is clearly for the young and healthy. That such cruising need not be confined to the sheltered waters has been proved time and again. The extremely courageous voyage by Frank Dye in 1961 in a Wayfarer dinghy (15 ft 10 in. overall, 6 ft 1 in. beam and 10 in. draught) from the north of Scotland to Bergen is an indication of the potentialities of open-boat sailing providing the crew is experienced and the boat is properly handled and carefully prepared.

As to what is the best sort of boat for this kind of cruising—well there are many viewpoints, and just as many boats. Such an authority as Conor O'Brien, who sailed round the world in *Saorse*, had some very pertinent things to say about the most suitable craft for a camping cruiser. His view was that the ideal camping cruiser should be the cheapest, plainest, lightest and yet strongest craft available. She must be easy to row and easy to sail and be between 12 ft and 18 ft in length. He also advocated a long, straight keel and a two-masted dipping lug rig. Other writers have agreed or disagreed with O'Brien according to their temper and their views. Any shallow boat with a roomy cockpit can be made into a camping cruiser, but those with straight keels and Scandinavian sterns are perhaps the best sea boats, have the easiest motion, and can most easily be hauled up on a beach without being damaged.

Many quite different kinds of boats can be used for this purpose. My first boat (I bought her complete for £5) was a 14 ft Medway sailing punt.

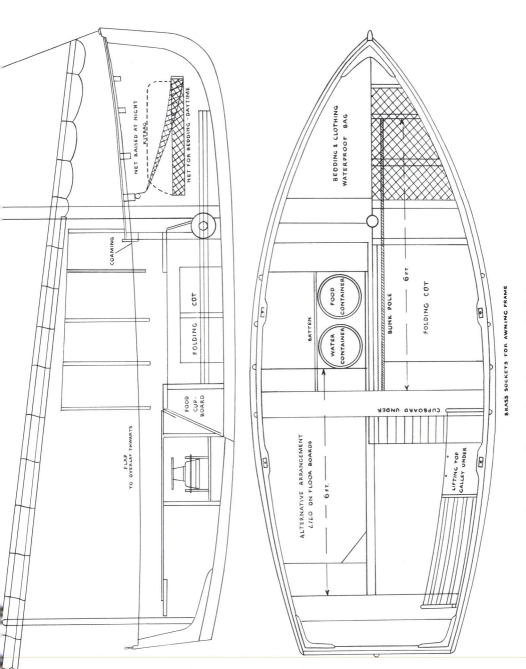

Fig. 27 14 ft camping dinghy. Plan showing alternative arrangements for sleeping. On the port side, an inflatable mattress rests on the floorboards in the cockpit, and on the starboard side there is a folding cot alongside the centreboard case

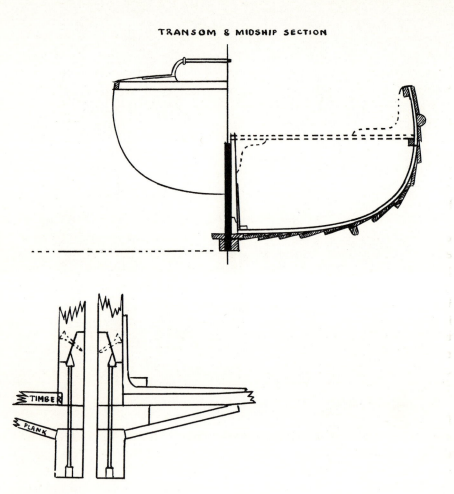

Fig. 28 Sections of 14 ft sailing dinghy,
and detail showing construction of
centreboard case

She was a hard-chined boat with sweet lines, a slightly rockered bottom
and an iron centreplate in a well-built oak case. She had a gunter lug and a
small foresail; she was a wonderful craft and as stiff as could be. I cannot
imagine a better boat for a beginner. The previous owner, an extremely
intrepid marine painter, had once sailed her from the Medway to Burnham,
on a day when larger and wiser boats were remaining at their moorings.
To save his tide he grounded on the Buxey Sands while the tide dropped,

boiled a kettle and had his tea. The little boat only drew a few inches of water so, when the tide made, he was soon afloat and away without damage. The weekend yachtsmen of Burnham were quite incredulous that so insignificant a craft had made such a voyage.

The gear in this boat was carried in waterproof tins which were bought from a paint manufacturer. An inflatable bed and all bedclothes were wrapped in waterproof bags and placed in a waterproof box. A simple awning was draped over the topped-up boom. The simplicity and unyachtiness of this little boat was one of her great virtues. She was soft and old when I had her, but I loved her dearly. She was completely open and as buoyant as a cork (see page 21).

Fourteen and 16 ft naval sailing dinghies are suitable for conversion to camping cruisers. They are constructed to a good specification and are excellent boats. The 14 ft dinghy has a beam of over 5 ft and a depth inside the gunwales of 2 ft amidships, and could be made into a useful little camping cruiser. It is designed to have a life-saving capacity of ten persons, so it will easily carry the load of a crew of two and their camping gear. There is about 14 in. clearance under the thwarts so the bedding could be laid on the floorboards aft, though there are side benches. There is about 5 ft between the stern thwart and the one at the after end of the centreboard case. All the cruising gear should be stowed inside waterproof containers which go on either side of the centreboard or under the foredeck.

Folding cots can be fitted to camping cruisers. A saddler will make them for you if you give him a paper pattern of the shape. Use stout Willesden canvas with brass eyelets down each side. One side will be laced to a stringer on the hull and the other side to a stout pole, which will slip into a special support when in use at night and during the day can be folded against the ship's sides. But in this case it would be difficult to install folding cots without altering the arrangements of the thwarts. If you do want to fit them, unfasten the side thwarts so that they can be used during the day but hinged up or lifted out at night. Two bunks just under 2 ft wide at the head could be fitted side by side; their poles would fit into sockets under the stern thwarts and on the sides of the centreboard case. The outboard sides of the bunks would lace to stringers on the boat's sides. Another arrangement would be to take the forward thwart out and to carry the bunks forward under the foredeck from either side of the centreboard case, the foredeck being extended aft of the mast to a beam at the forward end of the centreboard. As the forward thwart is to be removed the case will have to be supported with vertical beams on either side. This arrangement is perhaps

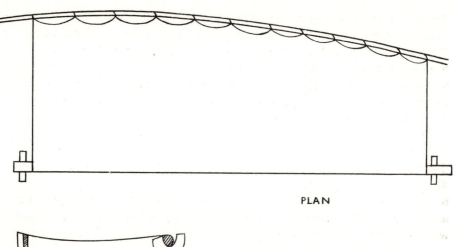

PLAN

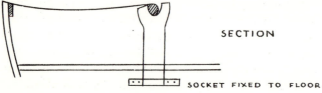

SECTION

SOCKET FIXED TO FLOOR

Fig. 29 Plan and section of folding cot.
The U-shaped upright slips into a socket
fitted on the side of the floor

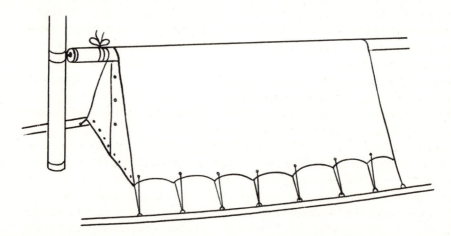

Fig. 30 Simple tent awning, resting on
the topped-up boom

in some ways the better, for it means that your awning need not come so far aft. The comfort of the camping cruiser chiefly depends on an awning that can be put up quickly and easily. The simplest awning is like a small bivouac tent, and is draped over the topped-up boom. The sides are fastened by lanyards to hooks or screw-eyes on the rail. The forward end has two overlapping flaps which clip onto fasteners. At the top, where the boom enters the tent, a wrapping like those on sail covers will make a watertight joint.

If you want sitting headroom under the awning you will have to stretch the cover over bent frames of ash or metal. They are easy to make and simple to put up, but they take up more room. Galvanised $\frac{1}{4}$ in. rod, or ash battens 2 in. $\times \frac{3}{4}$ in. would do very well. To bend the ash to shape steam it in a steam box and fix it between blocks of wood nailed to the floor. It will set in the right shape when it cools. The frames will fit in the brass sockets fastened to the outside of the coaming. The cover may be of light

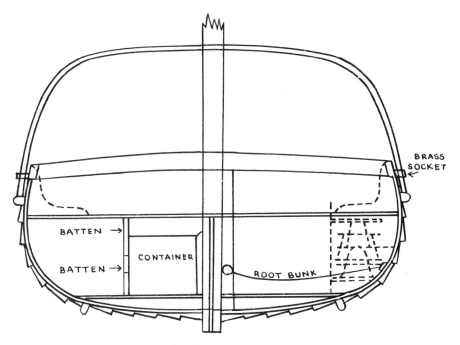

Fig. 31 Section of 14 ft camping dinghy, with awning on bent frames fitted into brass sockets on the outside of the gunwale

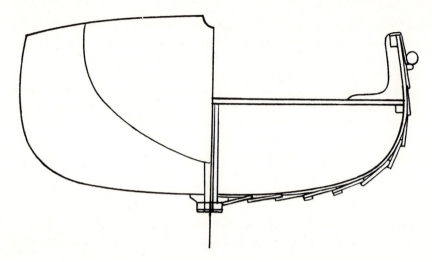

Fig. 32 10 ft Naval dinghy sections,
which show a very roomy hull

canvas or even balloon fabric. Strips of the same material through which
the frames pass are sewn to the inside. The covers must come down well
below the top of the coaming or the rain and spray will drive in. The forward end fastens to the coaming with press studs. The after end has two
flaps which can be laced on the inside. The whole thing folds up like the
hood of a car and can be stowed under the foredeck when not in use.

Comfort in any cruising boat depends on having a place for everything.
This is important enough in a cabin cruiser, but it is quite essential in a
camping cruiser.

Ten foot naval sailing dinghy
This really is the smallest boat you can possibly use as a cruiser. The
dimensions are 10 ft overall length, 4 ft 3 in. extreme breadth and 1 ft 10
in. depth amidships from the bottom of the keel to the top of the gunwale.
There are side benches at the stern and two thwarts with a daggerboard
case in between. The mast steps right up in the bows.

An energetic boy or girl can have a most enjoyable time cruising in
sheltered waters in this little boat. The gear should be kept as light as possible, and should be stowed in waterproof containers lashed down amidships. It may be necessary to have a tiller extension, for you will have to sit

Fig. 33 The sail plan is just a small
dipping lug

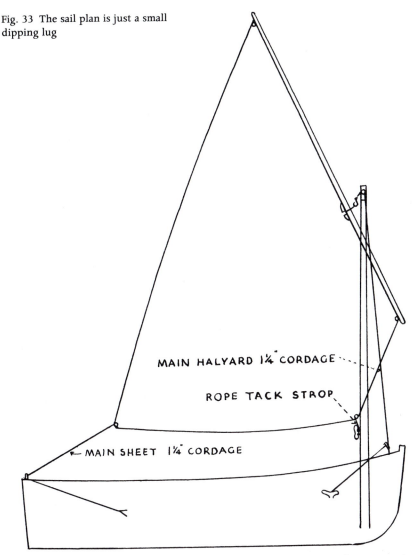

MAIN HALYARD 1¼" CORDAGE

ROPE TACK STROP

MAIN SHEET 1¼" CORDAGE

her out if she is going to cruise at all far afield. You can make an awning out
of balloon fabric that will roll up into quite a small bundle.

Camping and cruising in these little boats can be very pleasant and
exciting, especially if you can find a friend to join you in another boat of
the same kind. It all depends on making thorough preparations. Make sure
that your containers stow easily and that they are rustproof and water-

tight. Carry your matches and cooking apparatus—a primus stove or a solid alcohol stove—in a watertight box and always have a complete change of dry warm clothes with you. Finally, ensure that your boat has adequate buoyancy, either from metal tanks or inflatable bags. This buoyancy should be able to support the weight of the boat when full of water and the weight of the crew hanging onto it. Once again, your life may depend on this. Always sail in a life-jacket and never wear sea boots when afloat.

An 18 ft National dinghy needs a minimum of 400 lbs positive buoyancy. A 14 ft camping dinghy, loaded with gear, would need at least this much buoyancy. An 18 ft lifeboat used for this purpose would need from 550 to 650 lbs buoyancy.

Half-decked boats
Some half-decked, one-design boats will make good tabloid cruisers. Two bunks and sitting headroom are all they can offer in the way of accommodation, but this is far more comfort than you will find in any camping cruiser. If you are going to build a cabin, in order materially not to affect the boat's sailing performance keep the cabin roof low, and make it as light as is consistent with strength. If the beam of the boat is less than 6 ft 6 in. it is useless to attempt side decks; so build the topsides up from inside the old gunwale, give them a fair tumblehome and carry them fore and

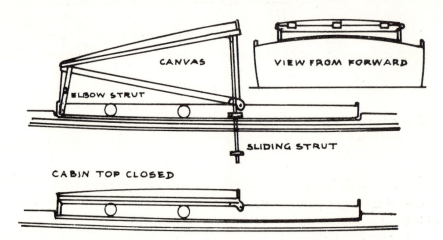

Fig. 34 The lifting cabin top designed by the late Mr Umfreville Lawes and published in *The Yachtsman* over fifty years ago. It is a most workable plan and suitable for sheltered waters

aft in a nice sweep. All the halyards should lead aft, so that you won't have to get out of the cockpit in a seaway. The cleats for the halyards and sheets should be arranged along the after end of the cabin top. The anchor cable, though fastened forward, should be stowed with the anchor under the cockpit benches.

Fitting a cabin top on a half-decked boat
If the side decks are very narrow, you can leave them in position and use the coamings as carlings. If they are wide, take them right out and make the cabin sides of $\frac{3}{8}$ in. mahogany or plywood, fastened outside the gunwales in the same way as the other planks, or *inside* the gunwales, using them as carlings. You will need good solid bulkhead frames fore and aft; and if you make the sliding hatchway as large as you can, the cabin will virtually become part of the cockpit if you leave the hatchway open when you are sailing.

Stiff and beamy boats have the most comfortable accommodation. If you want to go deep-water sailing, your boat must be seaworthy and be able to go to windward even when there is a nasty sea. Here the fine-lined boat has the advantage, for a light and beamy craft tends to stop dead every time it butts into a head sea. A watertight and spartan cabin (the less there is in it the less chance there is of squalor) and a self-draining cockpit are essential. Put buoyancy tanks in the bow and stern, so that if the boat fills she will still float.

The coastal and estuary cruiser should keep the half-decker's large cockpit. A raised cabin top will increase the headroom and an awning over the cockpit will give you extra sleeping space.

A lifting cabin top, like those on many of the boats on the Norfolk Broads, will make your cabin much more roomy and comfortable. By far the best type is that devised by Mr Umfreville Lawes and described in *The Yachtsman* sixty years ago.

This arrangement, which looks very flimsy, is actually strong enough to bear a man's weight. If the wind on the raised cabin makes the boat yaw about one can leave the windward end down and thus decrease the windage. The purpose of the lines attached to the elbow strut but not shown in Fig. 34 is to draw the canvas in out of the way when the top is lowered.

Pontoons
Ex-Service bridge pontoons come up for sale periodically. They are usually built of mahogany and plywood and can be successfully converted,

but into water-borne caravans or house boats rather than sea-going vessels. A most comfortable cabin can be added with two bunks and a proper galley with a dresser. Large opening Perspex windows will make it light and airy. The motor could be an 8 h.p. outboard clamped to a stern bracket.

Building a cabin onto a pontoon is quite simple. The coamings of the large well will make the carlings. Uprights 2 in. × 2in. should be checked into the carlings, and the transverse beams for the roof half-dovetailed to them with about a $\frac{3}{4}$ in. camber on top. Single sheets of marine plywood will do for the sides. The front will have to be made up of three pieces if it is to follow the shape of the well. The sheets of ply can be glued butt to butt. The sides should have about 3 in. of tumblehome and the forward end should have considerably more. The windows may be made of sheets of plate glass or Perspex. The top should be covered with marine ply. The pieces of plywood that you cut from the holes for the windows will make useful shutters during the winter when the boat is laid up. Make their fastenings of brass tubes set into the tops and bottoms of the windows. When the shutter is in place a brass bolt passes through the tube to a wing nut on the inside.

The plans of a pontoon houseboat conversion are shown on page 116. The inside can be extremely comfortable. This conversion was lined with mahogany and the galley was divided from the cabin by a bulkhead. The web fastenings amidships were taken out and slatted bunks were fitted about 8 in. above the floorboards.

The little craft was driven by a powerful outboard fastened to a bracket at the stern. She was steered by a wheel on the after portside bulkhead. In bad weather one could steer with the cabin door shut, almost as if one was driving a saloon car. This conversion was kept on the Stour, a very open river, where an east wind against the tide will turn up a very nasty sea, but the little boat seemed to manage. All the same she is not a sea-going craft.

Converting a 20 ft pontoon to a barge-yacht

A very ingenious conversion of a pontoon into a little barge-yacht was done some years ago by Mr W. Peake, of Manningtee. It must have meant a great deal of work, but I doubt if it cost very much, for most of the material came out of the pontoon itself.

She was an excellent boat for sheltered waters, but was not stable enough for seagoing.

This pontoon was made of mahogany resin-bonded ply, framed with 3 in.

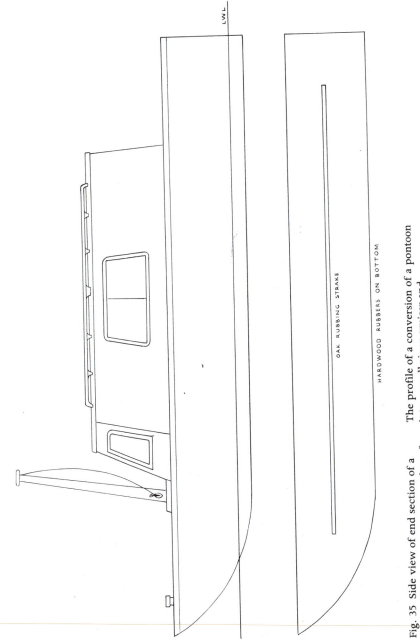

LWL

OAK RUBBING STRAKE

HARDWOOD RUBBERS ON BOTTOM

Fig. 35 Side view of end section of a plywood bridge pontoon. A number of these have come on the market and, if in good order, they can be made into quite useful river cruisers.

The profile of a conversion of a pontoon into a small river cruiser and houseboat by the late Mr W. G. Porter of Manningtree

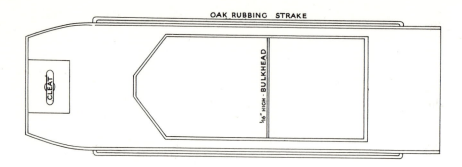

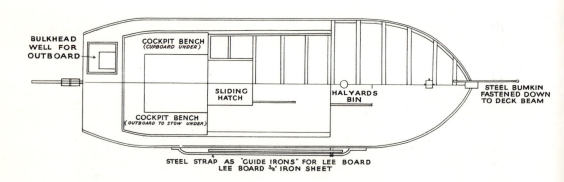

Fig. 36 Plans of pontoon and
barge-yacht

by $\frac{3}{4}$ in. mahogany. Here and there she had some first class oak, pine and teak. She was 20 ft long, with 5 ft 10 in. beam and 2 ft 5 in. deep. But her transom was absolutely square with no run whatever, and although her plywood bottom is immensely strong, it was merely two pieces of $\frac{7}{16}$ in. ply joined down the middle by two pieces of 2 in. by $\frac{3}{4}$ in. oak, by way of a keel. It could never carry a centreboard case without building in an entirely new keel.

This little barge ought to have been called *Vice Versa* for the original pontoon was turned back to front. The swimhead became the stern and the square transom the bow, but not before it had been taken out and the two sides wrapped together to make a stem. With the addition of leeboards, this was the basis of a little sailing barge.

Fig. 37 Sail plan of pontoon and
barge-yacht

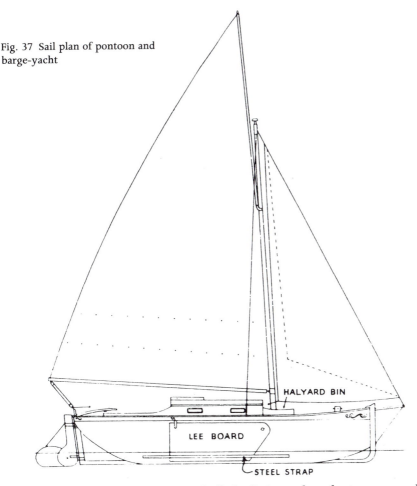

HALYARD BIN

LEE BOARD

STEEL STRAP

All the deck had to come off and all the fittings, then the transom and the
three aftermost frames. She was all brass and copper fastened, and most of
the screws came out with some persuasion. The copper nails were punched
out, and the two massive steel frames that ran along the sides from midships
to aft were removed. The salvage included some large sheets of ply from
the decks and transom, a good deal of oak, mahogany and teak framing,
and a box of brass screws.

The conversion work started with salvaged material and some second-
hand stuff. The transom deck beam was a piece of Australian teak 4 in. by
$2\frac{1}{2}$ in. Oak cheeks were screwed and resin-bonded to it and it was set up for
a stem with a laminated knee that also came out of the transom, using 4 ft
of 2 in. by 2 in. oak as a forward hog piece.

The original chines were of 2 in. by 2 in. oak. These were sawed off square about 5 ft from the stem and new curved ends were built up from two pieces of 2 in. by 1 in. ash each side. They were screwed down along the top of the old chines for about 4 ft. To have scarphed them would have involved taking another 4 ft of the boat to pieces. Oak would have been better than ash, but it was not to be had. The chines bent fairly well, after spending a few hours in a baker's oven wrapped up in wet sacks. A stringer, 4 in. by $\frac{5}{8}$ in. ash, was put in midway between the chine and the deck, and another, 2 in. by $\frac{3}{4}$ in., at deck level, taking it up about 5 in. to give her a sheer. The inner and outer chines were copper-nailed together, and then the sides were bent round and copper-nailed to the chines and stringers and screwed to two new frames, built between the partners and main frame and the stem.

A solid frame was built forward of midships in way of the mast. It consisted of a 7 in. by 2 in. pine floor laid flat with upright frames both sides, a 3 in. by 2 in. deck beam, and a 7 in. by 1 in. elm plank athwartships with a hole cut for the partners and a 2 in. by 2 in. beam on the forward side of it. This was to take care of all the new wringing strains which would be imposed by sailing, and which obviously were not contemplated when the pontoon was built.

Fillers were put between the floors to bring them up to the height of the forward hog piece and a 3 in. by 2 in. oak keelson was laid on them from right forward to well aft of amidships. This went over the 7 in. by 2 in. floor, and thus the thrust of the mast was taken by a very stout cross-piece.

The boat was then turned on her side, and the bottom bent up to the chines by main force to get the rise of the forefoot. It was fastened to the hog and chines with $1\frac{1}{2}$ in. and 2 in. brass screws.

The original frames had struts which came well out into the middle of the boat. These were cut out and replaced by plywood and mahogany webs.

A deadwood was built under the counter to increase the lateral resistance and help her to hold a course. It was made from an elm tumbrel shaft, bolted through an oak wedge and panelled over with plywood. The drop-plate rudder had been made for a 12 ft dinghy which did not survive the 1939–45 war.

The leeboards, which were about 7 ft long and 2 ft 4 in. wide at the bottom, were built up from 6 in. by $\frac{3}{4}$ in. oak and elm planks; the forward boards ran up and down parallel with the face and the back board lay diagonally behind them. They were weighted with sheet lead at the bottom. The brackets they hung from were made by having bolts welded into the heavy steel clasps which had originally been fixed to the transom and were intended for fastening two pontoons together when they were used for bridging.

Some unused ex-government sails, consisting of a canvas gunter mainsail of about 160 sq. ft and two foresails of about 70 sq. ft and 25 sq. ft were bought very cheaply, as was a spruce pole. This made a 22 ft mast and a boom and a gaff were then shaped from some Rumanian white wood. The boom was 15 ft long and $2\frac{1}{2}$ in. by 2 in. and the gaff 12 ft long and 3 in. by $1\frac{1}{2}$ in., both planed up to an oval section. The rigging was spliced and made up from government surplus wire and rope.

The little barge was well balanced, but she was a bit lightheaded, and she had to have about 15 cwt of scrap iron to ballast her, and the mast raked aft to give her some weather helm, before she would agree to come about!

The following winter a cabin was built onto her. The coamings were made from the remains of the plywood decking and the coach roof from 4 in. by $\frac{5}{8}$ in. tongue-and-groove deal, like the deck. The coach roof and deck were then canvased. The cabin was about 6 ft square, with sitting headroom, and there was a large forepeak. The sliding hatch was 3 ft wide to increase the cockpit space when sailing. The opening lights forward were made from plywood panels with openings in them, with Perspex panels sliding in oak rabbets to cover the openings.

For auxiliary power she had a 4 h.p. long-shaft British Anzani outboard, which worked through a watertight well cut through the afterdeck and counter. When not in use it stowed under the starboard cockpit seat, which was removable. The motor pushed her along very well.

Contrary to most people's expectations, she got to windward and showed little tendency to turn over. She was no flyer, but about five points off the wind with the weather chine just awash she travelled very well, and with the wind free it took quite a good boat to catch her. Once or twice a squall lifted the weather chine an uncomfortably long way out of the water, but luffing her up or easing the sheets always brought her back on an even keel. As a ditch-crawler she had many good points. If she went aground the crew stepped over the side into ankle-deep water, and pushed her off. She always floated again when relieved of the weight of the crew.

Converting an 18 ft lifeboat to a 2-berth sloop

An 18 ft lifeboat does not make such an effective sailing cruiser as a 26 ft or 24 ft one, but, with care, a nice little cruising sloop can be designed. The

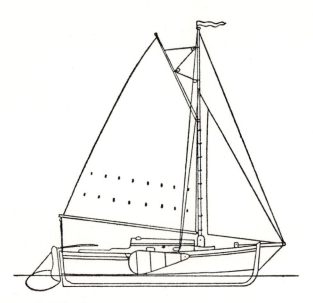

Fig. 38 18 ft lifeboat leeboard sloop

Board of Trade lifeboats are 18 ft in length, 6 ft 3 in. in beam and 2 ft 3 in. inside depth amidships. They have four thwarts and the normal sail area is 86 sq. ft.

The general method of conversion will be as for the 26 ft lifeboat, but it is better to do without side decks and carry the cabin top right across. You can raise the freeboard by carrying the planking up higher, which will mean fastening false timbers alongside the old ones and fitting a new gunwale. A simpler method is to screw the cabin sides to the inside of the gunwale; and it is just as firm and effective a way of fastening. Each side should be made of one plank of $\frac{3}{8}$ in. mahogany carried forward and aft in a gradual sweep. Take off the capping so that you can see for certain that you are screwing into the timbers and filling pieces and not just through the gunwale lining. You can fit a new capping, glue it up to the cabin sides with marine glue, and fasten it down onto the gunwale. There should be a doubling piece of $1\frac{1}{2}$ in. by 1 in. along the cabin top into which 1 in. square beams can be checked with half-dovetails. Use a heavier beam at the forward and after ends. The forward bulkhead can be a single $\frac{5}{8}$ in. plank of mahogany. Aft it should be $\frac{1}{2}$ in. tongue and groove mahogany.

You can have either a false keel or leeboards. I strongly advise leeboards. The Dutch have used them for hundreds of years, but they have never been very popular in British waters. E. F. Knight praises leeboards in *Small Boat Sailing*. He fitted them to an old P. & O. lifeboat, which he sailed from Hammersmith to Copenhagen and back, cruising round the Zuider Zee, coasting up the Friesian Islands, winding in and out of many pleasant fjords, straits and islands of the Baltic. (His full account of this voyage is in *The Falcon on the Baltic*.) With her varnished teak sides and oak leeboards she looked very well, and her sailing powers were as excellent as her appearance. I had an 18 ft Matelot class sloop some years ago, fitted with leeboards that were efficient and easy to operate. They were made of single planks of oak, weighted at the bottom with lead and bound round the edges with brass bands. They hung on universal joints. It is no good fastening leeboards with a single bolt, for there is a strong outward thrust on the windward board if it happens to be down. Leeboards should be flat on the outside, but have an aerofoil curve on the inside. There should be a chafing piece at least the length of the leeboard fitted to the side of the boat about three strakes down from the gunwale.

A small block is shackled to the trailing edge and the halyard leads up to a block on the cabin side and then aft to a cleat. It is unseamanlike to leave the weather board trailing like a broken wing, but if you are sailing single handed in narrow waters it may be necessary, and it does not affect the boat's performance to windward. In very shallow waters where you cannot let the leeboards right down, it is surprising what a difference a few inches of board will make.

A drop rudder will help the boat to sail to windward. The blade of the rudder on our Matelot was made of $\frac{1}{4}$ in. bronze. Galvanised iron would have done just as well. A light galvanised chain shackled to a hole drilled in the trailing edge, and was joined to a piece of line just before it reached a sheave in the rudder immediately under the tiller head. The line lead through and was made fast to a cleat underneath the tiller.

If you have leeboards instead of a false keel you will not need such heavy floors. Two in. by 3 in. floors at 2 ft intervals should be strong enough. The tongue and groove or $\frac{1}{4}$ in. marine ply bulkhead is a rigid enough framing for the cuddy. The foredeck does not need a heavy king plank like that on the 26 ft boat; it would be better to cover it in marine ply.

The little cuddy will have about 4 ft headroom and will just accommodate two 6 ft 2 in. bunks if they are carried up under the foredeck, and still leave a space of 2 ft 6 in. on either side of the cabin for the galley and food cupboards.

The 18 ft lifeboat has rather full lines and had best be rigged as a gaff

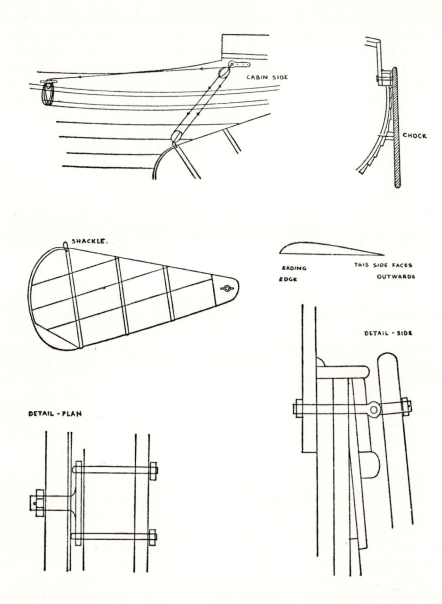

Fig. 39 *Top left*: Side view of leeboard, showing block and tackle
Top right: Sectional view of leeboard, showing chock

Middle: Plan and section views of leeboard
Bottom: Plan and section views, details of fastenings

sloop. I have given her a long luff and a short gaff. An even longer luff and a curved gaff like the Dutch rig would be attractive, but not so easy to make.

If you do without side decks you can have a good large cockpit, perfect for day sailing, and with plenty of room to get at the engine. The leeboards make the boat look rather Dutch, so why not go the whole hog? If the hull is in good condition, and you think the trouble worth taking, burn off the topside paint, taking care not to char the wood, rub it down, stop any holes with wooden plugs or matching stopping, rub it all over with linseed oil, and then varnish. Varnish the oak leeboards as well. Paint the decks a cold stone colour and have a tanned mainsail and jib. The effect is delightful and quite simple to achieve.

The conversion of a 26 ft lifeboat to a ketch-rigged cruiser

There are many ways of converting a ship's lifeboat, and as many rigs. I converted my lifeboat into a gaff-rigged ketch; Mr Van der Werf converted his into a gaff cutter. We both felt that the lifeboat hull was unsuited to a tall bermudan rig.

Now, though the gaff ketch rig is not ideal for getting to windward, a lifeboat's hull, with its full run aft, is even less weatherly than the rig. Something must be done to make her less leewardly. As a compromise, I drew out a moderate addition to the keel in the form of a long false wooden keel, giving her a keep depth of 11 in. She was to have inside ballast, which is, of course, simpler and cheaper than an outside ballast keel. I decided that ultimately she would have an auxiliary engine. Thus she would have a moderate performance into the wind, but when wind and tide were both foul she could come in under sail and power.

As the false keel was to be only 6 in. deep at the centre, I could not vary the shape much. We were trimming the boat down by the stern, so I decided on a false keel of simple shape with the greatest depth amidships. It carried the present curve of the forefoot down in a gentle sweep, increasing to its full depth 8 ft aft, that is, just under the mainmast. This depth continued for the next 13 ft aft, and then tapered fairly abruptly up to the sternpost. (This has been modified in the plans.)

Once the lines and sail plan are settled, the cabin is the most important thing about a cruising boat. It can taken an infinite variety of shapes and sizes. For the lifeboat it could be in the form of a raised deck amidships; it could be a trunk with side decks; it could be a trunk extending forward, with the mainmast sticking up through it; it could have a doghouse aft, and so on. We thought round the problem and eventually decided on the most conventional, a trunk amidships. In some ways I would have preferred

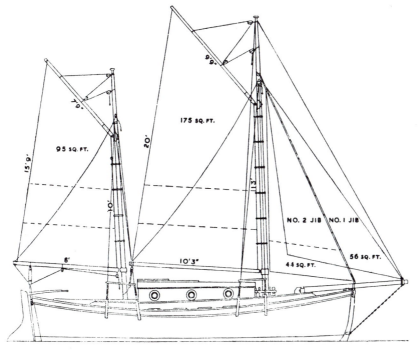

Fig. 40 Sail plan of 26 ft lifeboat
converted to a ketch

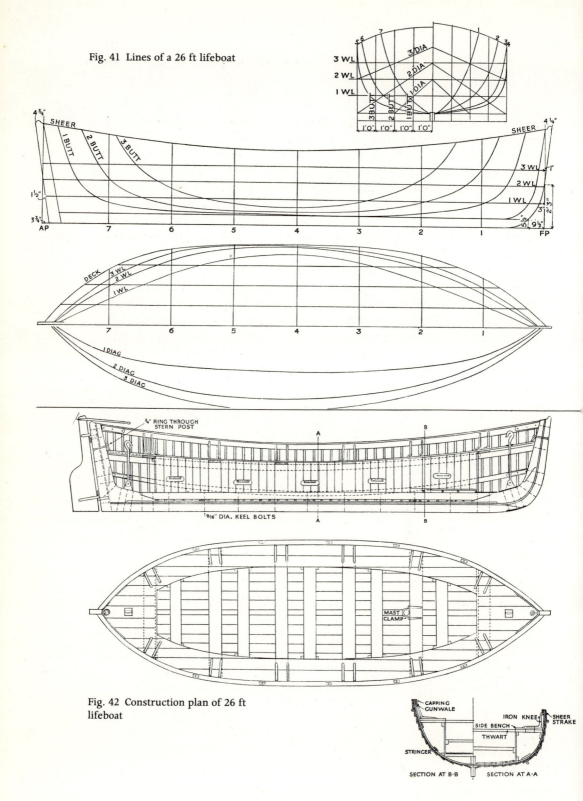

Fig. 41 Lines of a 26 ft lifeboat

Fig. 42 Construction plan of 26 ft
lifeboat

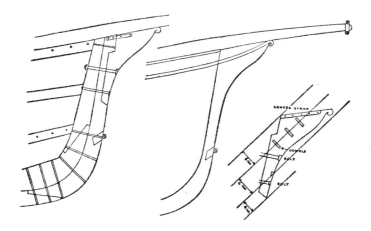

Fig. 43 *Left*: Construction of stem with fiddlehead, in one piece, scarphed and bolted to original stem

Right: Construction of the fiddlehead if made up of three 9 in. by 3 in. planks
Centre: The completed fiddlehead with rubbing strake carried up to the fillet in a fair curve

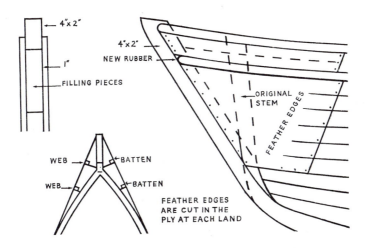

Fig. 44 Built-up stem for 26 ft lifeboat

built-up topsides and raised deck amidships, but although this method gives strength to a yacht originally built on this plan with her timbers running right up to the top of the cabin, in our case it meant false timbers, through-bolted to the old ones or to the planks—a weak construction. Besides, the rigid framework of the side decks would help strengthen her.

A lifeboat hull, married to a ketch rig, with sturdy spars and a well-considered colour scheme, makes a most likeable little ship. The secret of successful conversion is to try to make all the new features an integral part of the boat and not just a series of unconnected additions.

The first thing was to eliminate the saddle-backed line by a well-planned bulwark rail; the next was to tackle the stem. I believe the best-looking stem would be the old-fashioned, fiddlehead cutwater, grafted on to her straight stempost—this would more than counterbalance her straight stern. Fiddleheads are rare now in British waters but are still to be seen around the North American coasts, where they have never gone out of fashion or favour.

Another way of improving the lifeboat's appearance is to give her a false stem. This is not a very difficult operation and has been done most successfully by Mr Henry Smart, a Woodbridge boatbuilder. And as for such a stem not being seaworthy, his ex-30 ft lifeboat has been to the Mediterranean and back, and has taken more than one good bang in Dutch locks. The false bow for this conversion was made up of a framework, very securely fastened to the existing stem and bows of the boat and then covered in plywood, which was most successfully faired into the lines of the planking. The detailed drawings shown in Fig. 44 explain this better than words. What a difference such a bow can make to the look of a conversion! No one would guess the origins of this powerful-looking motor-sailer, with her piratical black topsides and purposeful air.

Chiefly through lack of timber we did not give our 26 ft lifeboat a fiddlehead or a false bow, but left her with her straight stem and a 6 in. bulwark rail. With her trim aft, her lines improved considerably.

As one of the main features of a cruising conversion is the cabin, much thought has to be given to it. Apart from not trying to cram quarts or gallons into pint pots, there are certain rules to observe in drawing the lines of a cabin trunk. The profile should under most conditions parallel the waterline or slope down towards the bow. The traditional Dutch cabin as seen in many of their converted boeiers and botters has a marked concave curve to the profile, with the roof of the cabin sweeping up aft. Hogged profiles are not very pretty.

How often has one seen converted ships' lifeboats with a thing like a hen-coop doing duty for a cabin! In a shoal-draught 26 ft boat *you cannot get standing headroom in the cabin,* so there is no point in having more than sitting headroom. We planned to make the cabin 4 ft 6 in. high in the middle and 4 ft at the sides, and to give the sides plenty of tumblehome. Though they stood a clear 14 in. from deck to roof, they didn't look unsightly, for this height was reduced by the 6 in. bulwark rail. To break the hard up-right line of the forward cabin bulkhead, we built a nice little fife rail round the foot of the mast. Avoid streamlining your cabin top, or it will look ridiculously incongruous, sitting on a lifeboat hull.

We chocked the lifeboat up on some old sleepers, with 4 in. by 2 in. legs bolted to the plank under her rail to keep her upright. First we gave her a good scrub out and then we drew the keel bolts. When these were drawn we could estimate the length of the new bolts, taking into account the depth of the false keel at each station. Some were $\frac{1}{2}$ in. and others $\frac{5}{8}$ in. bolts of lengths varying from 14 in. to 20 in. I tried to buy some, but failed, so I got a local engineering firm to make them up from mild steel bar. They cost ninepence each.

They should have been galvanised, but we were in a hurry and decided to use the fisherman's method of rustproofing. We warmed each bolt with a blowlamp (to open the pores of the iron, they said) and then dipped it in tar. This is certainly most effective. While our tar was hot, we put a good coating on the top of the new false keel and also on the bottom of the old keel. The new false keel had to be made in three pieces and scarphed together. A piece of canvas, soaked in tar, was placed in the scarph joint.

We did not bore for the bolts until the keel was in position, as the old bolt holes were at various angles.

We jacked the boat up, slipped the new false keel into position and then lowered the boat onto it. From inside we bored through the keelson with a long gimlet bit, and then from underneath the new keel drilled larger holes to countersink the bolt heads and so drove the bolts up from underneath, a nice driving fit. Finally we countersunk the nuts, gave them a coating of tar and buried them in a stopping of putty. Thus the top of the keelson presented a smooth surface, for it was not to be covered by floorboards in the cabin.

Incidentally, when all the bolts were drawn, the keelson was free so that we could clean out and tar underneath it.

With the false keel fixed, we started to make the floors. These are timbers that stretch athwart the bottom of the boat and provide much of her

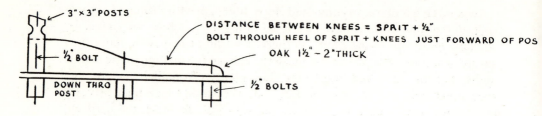

Fig. 45 Method of fastening bitts to
deckbeams and king plank

strength. There is a formidable wringing strain in any sailing boat. In the
lifeboat's original form, without the floors, lateral stresses on the keel are
transmitted from the false keel through the bolts to the keelson, which was
originally intended merely for longitudinal strength. So we decided to slot
eight floors over the keelson. The two largest, of 9 in. by $2\frac{1}{2}$ in. oak, were
for the cabin bulkheads. The floors for the middle of the cabin and cockpit
were of 9 in. by $1\frac{1}{2}$ in. oak, and those forward and aft of the cabin were cut
from the old thwarts.

There are various ways of fixing the floors. If they are not too massive
they can be bolted to the keelson and screwed or nailed to the planks.

Alternatively, since the keelson has little structural value except to
prevent the lifeboat from sagging when hanging in davits, you can take out
the keelson altogether and cut the floors to fit flush with the skin of the
boat. To fit floors so that they lie closely over the lands might seem a rather
difficult undertaking. However, it is not very difficult to make templates of
plywood or even cardboard. These can be cut roughly to shape, then placed
in position and the line of the planks, including the lands, scribed in by
dividers. A double check should be made at each land, taking a vertical
measurement by rule. Amidships, for a 3 in. wide floor both sides would be
the same; but near stem or stern, two sets of templates should be made, for
both sides of the floor. When fitted in position the floors are screwed to the
planks from the outside and through-bolted to the keel.

The timber of the keelson might well be used for the false keel, for the
keelson (or rider-keelson) of a 26 ft lifeboat is usually 6 in. deep, though
I have seen them twice as deep as that. If you do remove the keelson the
bolts supporting the keel must be taken right through the floors, which
should be fitted close to the skin of the boat alongside the timbers. The
floors can end at the stringers and should be clench-fastened for 6 in. from
the ends, and then fastened through every land with heavy brass screws.

Bilge keels

Bilge keels are a reasonable alternative (or addition) to the false keel. For the 26 ft boat they did not need to be more than about 9 ft long. If you have a false keel they need only be about 10 in. deep, but they should be 18 in. deep if they are to provide all the lateral resistance. They are fastened at the turn of the bilge so that they lie outwards at an angle of about 30°, thus being at their deepest when the boat is heeled. They should be bolted through a 4 in. by 2 in. stringer cut somewhat longer than the keels and set on top of the timbers. Packing pieces must be fitted between the planking and stringer in the way of the bolts, and the bolts should be spaced 1 ft apart. The bilge keels should be $2\frac{1}{2}$ in. thick, shaped to the hull, and should run straight fore and aft, slightly toed in, and stand out square from the planking. It should be possible to fit them to the face of one plank and avoid having to cut over the lands. The first plank inside the old grips is the best place for the bilge keel. The 9 ft long bilge keels should have the centres about amidships, and the stringers about 1 ft longer at either end. The bolts will be $\frac{3}{8}$ in. or $\frac{1}{2}$ in. steel.

Bilge keels are an absolute boon for shoal waters as they allow the boat to lie on the mud or even on a hard bottom at a very slight angle of heel. This may make a night aground a comfortable instead of a hideous experience.

In the cabin we fitted bearers for the floorboards between the centre floor and the bulkheads. To get the maximum headroom, we dropped the floorboards so that they came flush with the top of the keelson and the centre floor; thus the bearers had to be $\frac{7}{8}$ in. below this level to allow for the thickness of the floorboards, which were also supported by fillets of $1\frac{1}{2}$ in. square stuff nailed to the bulkheads and floors.

I cut the floorboards from the long planks that had covered the side lockers. They were of $\frac{7}{8}$ in. red pine and curved on one side, so I had to do a good deal of juggling to get enough flooring out of them.

Repairs to clench-planking

Though we had no repairs to make to our 26 ft lifeboat's planking, the next clench-planked boat I had was dropped when being unloaded off a lorry, and two of the bottom planks were stove in. I viewed this with dismay, but the repairs proved not to be very difficult. The damage covered an area of about 15 in. by 9 in. so we cut out about twice that width and punched out the fastenings of two planks. To do this the rooves were cut off and the nails driven outward, taking care not to enlarge the nail holes. The broken bits of plank were carefully removed. New planks of the same thickness and

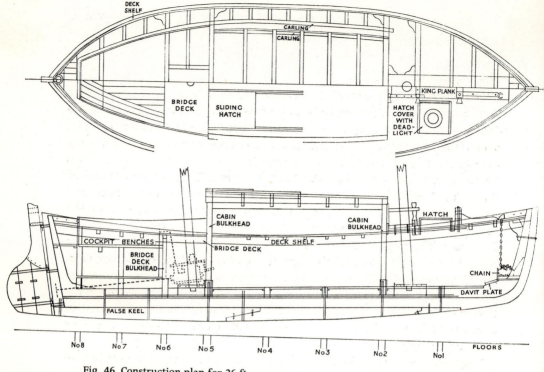

Fig. 46 Construction plan for 26 ft lifeboat ketch

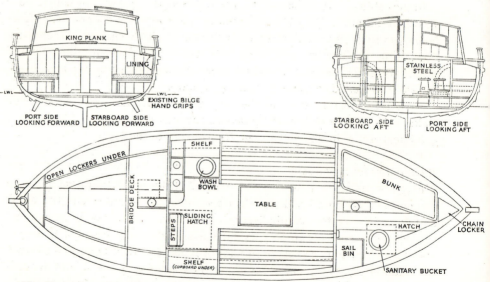

Fig. 47 Accommodation plan for 26 ft lifeboat ketch

wood were laid under the ones they were to replace and carefully scribed.

As the old planks had been cut out (by a padsaw) with vertical cuts, the length of two scarphs had to be added. These scarphs were about 6 in. long. They were simple enough to cut in the new wood, but had to be sawed, chiselled and planed in either end of the planks still fastened to the boat. After trial fitting, the scarphs were coated with glue and the planks were then sprung into position. They were then drilled, nailed and riveted.

As a result of this clumsy handling, two of the timbers were also broken. The repairs to these were also not difficult. The rooves were again cut off and the nails punched out to two strakes beyond the replaced planks. Some straight-grained Canadian rock elm was cut to size and wrapped in boiling cloths until it was thoroughly pliable and softened; it was bent and clamped into position alongside the position of the broken timbers, thus doubling up the timbers beyond the areas of damage. The nail holes were bored before putting the new wet timbers in. The nails were then driven through from outside, whilst the wood was still hot and wet; they needed no further drilling. They were then riveted in the usual manner. After the timbers had set, there were one or two extra fastenings. For these we drilled both planks and timbers to avoid any danger of splitting.

Cabin bulkhead framework, the deck shelf, deck beams, king plank, deck planking

With the floors fixed and the floorboards in position, we had something to move about on. The next job was to fit the uprights for the cabin bulkheads. These were of $1\frac{1}{2}$ in. by 9 in. oak, cut to fit the curve of the ship's sides and to fit over the stringers and under the fore-and-aft shelf which has to carry the deck beams. This shelf was made from a long plank of BC pine, 4 in. deep and 1 in. thick. It curved round from stem to sternpost at the deck line, that is at about 9 in. down from the top of the stem, but only 1 in. below the gunwale amidships, for the deck had much less sheer than the rail. Thus it abutted the inside of the gunwale amidships, but as it approached the ends of the boat it was no longer supported, and filling pieces had to be fitted. When these were in place, we clamped the shelf into position and clench-fastened it with 4 in. stout copper nails.

We now marked where the beams were to come and mortised the shelf to receive them. We had decided on a $1\frac{1}{2}$ in. camber in the deck, so the beams had to be cut to this shape, both on top and underneath. The beams on each side of the masts should be especially heavy, with an area of cross-section about three times that of the ordinary beams. There should be strong partners, about 2 in. by 9 in. in size, between the beams, with $\frac{3}{8}$ in. tie-bolts alongside them.

The beams were dropped into position and screwed down to the shelf with $2\frac{1}{2}$ in. 14 gauge brass screws. A stout knee of 3 in. oak was through-bolted to the apron, with its upper edge 1 in. below the top of the shelf. A small triangular piece rested on this bracket and joined the two shelves. This was to be the seat for the forward end of the king plank. But first we had to remove a large ring-bolt from the stem by cutting one end off and punching it out through the hole.

The king plank was a massive piece of oak, 9 ft by 15 in. by 2 in. It had to be somewhat curved in section, so we planed the underside concave to fit the slight camber of the deck beams, and then planed the top to match. The foredeck had 2 or 3 in. of sheer, so the king plank had to be clamped down to make it follow the line of the deck beams. We found it exerted a strong lifting force on the two middle deck beams, so, to counteract this, we made four little locking cleats which fitted under the beams and under the shelf.

Hanging and lodging knees
The ideal wood for any knee is a naturally-grown crook of a hardwood such as oak or cherry. Grown crooks are very difficult to come by, so some kind of alternative is necessary. By far the simplest is to use two or three pieces of $\frac{5}{8}$ in. marine ply cut to size, glued together and faced with $\frac{3}{8}$ in. Canadian rock elm steamed to shape and glued onto the front. The knee is drilled for bolts or long nails, which are then riveted through after the knee has been glued into position. This makes a very strong and rigid support either for

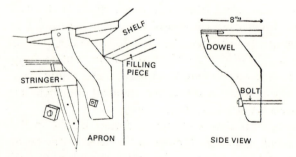

Fig. 48 Hanging stem knee for supporting the kingplank. This makes a very firm seating

hanging or lodging knees. A simpler method for lodging knees is to nail or screw a gusset of marine ply to the bearers and carlings.

Before fastening the king plank, we fitted lodging knees between the shelf and the after side of the forward bulkhead. They were bolted to the bulkhead beam and right through the shelf and topsides. When the king plank had been fastened down to the beams with 5 in. copper nails, the ship had a very strong and rigid foredeck. This strength would be further increased by the planking.

Before planking the deck we had to fit the carlings, which support the side decks and the cabin sides; they were of larch, 2 in. by $2\frac{1}{2}$ in., and had to be slotted into the forward and after bulkheads, and to be curved to follow the line of the deck.

The forward bulkhead had a simple frame consisting of the two outside supports already mentioned and a transverse beam cut to the camber of the deck which slotted into the top of them and into the shelf.

This bulkhead is most important, for not only does it take the thrust of the king plank and support the side decks, but it is the last complete transverse support at deck level until you come to the after bulkhead 8 ft further aft. The after bulkhead is not, of course, a complete transverse member, for it is broken by the cabin door; though this could be obviated by having a bridge deck immediately aft of the bulkhead, which would involve fitting a sliding hatch. The joinery in the after bulkhead has to be very carefully done if it is to be a strong transverse support. The left-hand diagram in Fig. 00 shows the general construction of this bulkhead. The

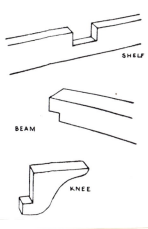

Fig. 49 Details of shelf, beam and knee

main framework was of $1\frac{1}{2}$ in. by 4 in., and $1\frac{1}{2}$ in. by $4\frac{1}{2}$ in. English oak. The cabin beam was of 1 in. timber with a 5 in. camber. It is cut from an 8 ft plank and is 3 in. deep in the centre, tapering to 2 in. at the ends.

Vertical supports for the forward bulkhead had now to be fitted. They were mortised into the under side of the beam and spiked on to the floor. The king plank was then firmly fastened down to the beams with screws as an addition to the through-fastenings which had already been put in.

The deck was planked with tongue-and-groove $\frac{3}{4}$ in. BC pine, and the planks were spiked down to the bearers with $1\frac{1}{2}$ in. galvanised boat nails. These were driven home into previously bored holes. These flat-headed nails do not need punching home. If galvanised wire nails are used, their heads have to be driven below the surface and puttied.

An alternative to tongue-and-groove planking is marine ply. I am not very fond of this material but if it is of the best quality and properly sealed on both flat surfaces and on the edges, it can provide a very strong deck. Where two pieces abut, a flat scarph should be cut and both surfaces be well coated with a phenolic resin glue and finally glued together. I do not recommend gluing the deck into position, that is, to the beams, in case it ever has to be taken up. Our deck was fastened at 4 in. intervals with flat-headed boat nails. Whether or not you canvas a plywood deck is a matter of choice; there is something to be said for and against this. For, you save wear on the ply; against, your deck is much more liable to rot if rainwater gets under the canvas.

The carlings needed care in fitting. We used some well-seasoned larch, $2\frac{1}{8}$ in. square. We clamped a 12 ft length where the cabin sides were to come and saw that there was a considerable curve, even amidships. To keep the distance from the topsides constant, we cut some 12 in. pieces and then clamped the carling onto them. When it was in position on top of the beams either side of the cabin, we marked up the mortises for the side deck beams, so that they should each be at the correct angle to the carling. We also marked the mortises in the two main deck beams to ascertain the correct angle. The mortises were then cut to a depth of 2 in. and the carling was likewise cut and slipped into position. If you have any tumblehome to the cabin sides the carling has to be tipped to the same angle, or a wedge-shaped batten screwed to the inside. The tumblehome in our cabin was $2\frac{1}{2}$ in. This meant that the top of the carling would not be level and so had to be planed to a bevel. To increase the strength of the short deck beams under the side decks, we made them in the form of brackets, 2 in. deep at the carlings, and 5 in. at the shelf.

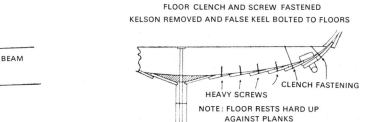

FLOOR CLENCH AND SCREW FASTENED
KELSON REMOVED AND FALSE KEEL BOLTED TO FLOORS

SLOT IN SHELF

BEAM

KNEE

CLENCH FASTENING
HEAVY SCREWS
NOTE: FLOOR RESTS HARD UP
AGAINST PLANKS

Fig. 50 As the king plank exerts an upward pull, interlocking knees are fitted

Fig. 51 Floors and false keel. Method of fastening

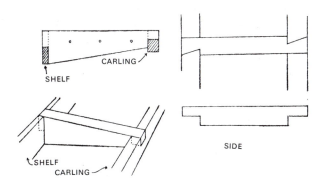

CARLING

SHELF

SHELF
CARLING

SIDE

Fig. 52 Side deck beams are cut to the depth of the deck shelf on the outside and to the carling on the inside. They are half-slotted. Cockpit beams, showing half-dovetailing in plan and half-slotting in the side view

The after bulkhead and bridge deck bulkhead are panelled, inside and out, with tongue-and-groove planking from the locker fronts of the original boat. Inside the cabin it is best set back against fillets so that the oak framing remains visible. On the outside it overlaps the frames. If you are using new wood, carry the planks right up from the floor to the cabin top; but if you are using up old stuff from the locker fronts overlap the horizontal joints with half-round beading.

The cockpit carlings

The cockpit carlings, unlike the cabin carlings, do not follow the line of the gunwale. Thus at the after cabin bulkhead the side decks are 15 in. wide, but at the after end of the cockpit they are only 9 in. wide. These carlings are also upright, as there need be no tumblehome to the cockpit coamings. They are fastened fore and aft to the cabin bulkhead and deck beams by slotting them into supports fixed to the beams. As there is a very marked curve, we had to dovetail the side deck beams into the carling and the shelf to stop the carling from springing out of position. With the carlings and the side deck beams in position, the planking can be completed. The outside plank can be screwed on. Corner posts must then be fastened to the carlings

Though cabin trunk sides in most yachts built in England are usually fastened with the trunk sides inside the carlings, a different method commonly used on the other side of the Atlantic has much to recommend it. That is, the cabin trunk actually sits on the deck. On my present boat, the cabin sides are fastened in this manner, which certainly produces, I am sure, not only a perfectly strong structure but also an absolutely watertight one. It involves using two carlings (3 in. wide by $1\frac{1}{2}$ in. thick) instead of one, with the deck passing between the two. To hide this sandwich appearance in the cabin, a covering board of $\frac{1}{2}$ in. wood of the same material as the cabin sides can be used. This should project $\frac{1}{2}$ in. above the top carling, thus making a useful ledge 3 in. wide. The deck canvas, if any, should be taken under the trunk sides and turned up between the trunk planking and the carling. This is well coated with paint and makes a watertight joint. If the deck ever needs recanvasing, cut off the canvas with a sharp knife on the outside of the cabin sides. The aft bulkhead should be fastened in the usual way; that is, screwed to the inside of a deck beam.

The cabin trunk

The cabin trunk is assembled in the following order: first the carlings are fixed; then the cabin sides, if they are all in one piece, are screwed on the carlings. If the cabin sides are made up of several planks, only the bottom plank can be screwed on. Corner posts must then be fastened to the carlings and to the cabin sides, after which the beams and knees across the ends of the cabin trunk can be fitted. Any remaining side planks are screwed into position with temporary uprights fixed to each plank to prevent it springing. A good strong carling will be needed for the junction between the cabin sides and top ($2\frac{1}{2}$ in. by $1\frac{1}{4}$ in.). It is fastened straight to the cabin side. It is indicated as a doubling piece in Fig. 54. The roof beams are cut to the

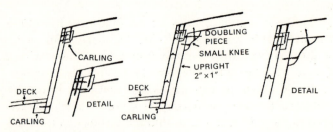

Fig. 53 The cabin top structure and methods of fastening

camber of the cabin and half-slotted and checked into the carlings. The top of each beam is bevelled to match the fore and aft camber, and the underneath is chamfered and curved to match the top. The ports or windows should be cut now before the roof is planked. Mark a circle with a compass, drill a $\frac{1}{2}$ in. hole, and cut out the circle with a padsaw. If the windows are any other shape mark them out accordingly, and proceed in the same way. With the framework in position, start laying the roof planks. Lay one plank in the dead centre and work on alternate sides. Clamp the planks close together, and fasten each end with two screws and then nail and screw them to alternate deck beams. To strengthen the roof still further, fix half-round battens across underneath at 6 in. intervals between the deck beams and screw them into position. Make sure that the uprights which are now to be fitted sit hard up under each beam and that their backs are bevelled to take any curve in the cabin sides.

If marine ply is used instead of planking, the half-round battens can be dispensed with.

After bulkhead and bridge deck bulkhead
These we panelled, inside and out, with the tongue-and-groove planking that had been the old locker fronts in the lifeboat. Apart from nail holes, which we filled with putty, it was in excellent condition. We cut a large window on the port side (see photograph) into which we fitted a sheet of $\frac{1}{4}$ in. Perspex; it was screwed to a simple 1 in. by $\frac{5}{8}$ in. batten and made an excellent leakproof window.

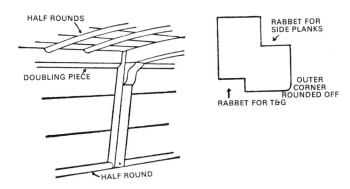

Fig. 54 *Left*: View of cabin side and roof, showing vertical upright which is only necessary if the cabin side is made up of more than one plank
Right: Corner post for cabin, sectional view

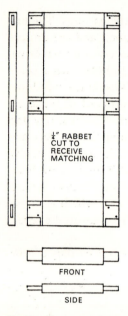

FRONT

SIDE

Fig. 55 The construction of a
panelled door. All uprights and
transverse members are mortised into
each other. A $\frac{1}{4}$ in. rabbet is cut to
receive matching

Doors

The door may be either single or double, or it may consist of slides. I have
tried all three and have come to the conclusion that there is a lot to be said
for slides, which are easier to make. But if you insist on hinged doors, make
them narrow double ones that will fold back out of the way. If you do have
slides, mark them in some way, so that you can tell in which order they go.

Buy your brass hinges from a ship chandler and make sure that the pins
are monel metal or brass. The brass hinges one buys from an ordinary
hardware shop invariably have steel pins which will rust solid in less than a
season.

Forehatch

Forehatches should be at least as wide as your shoulders; that is, a minimum
inside measurement of 21 in. This is one of the most leak-prone openings
in any boat. If the hatch cover beds down on a strip of rubber, this certainly
helps. A more effective method is to follow Maurice Griffiths's design of a

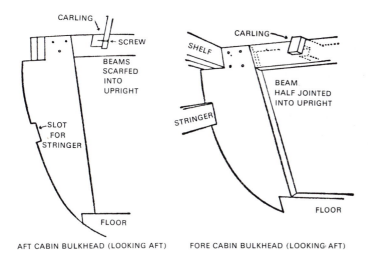

Fig. 56 Details of bulkhead framing

double coaming hatchway. This is rather more difficult to construct. I think an improvement would be to use the same method of construction as for the cabin trunk, with double carlings. However, one would need at least one filling piece in the middle of each side, level with the top of the outer coaming, to give complete rigidity to the inner coaming. The hatch could be fastened down with a hasp and staple and padlock. It is most important that these waterways between the coamings are liberally treated with preservative and then painted.

Cockpit floor
The cockpit floor is in two levels (there being no bridge deck), for we found that when the side benches were at the right height for steering, the floor was an uncomfortably long way off. Cross-bearers similar to the floors were cut from old thwarts and fitted. The lifeboat's original floorboards were laid on top. The wooden straps underneath this large section were cut in two places so that one could lift out a V-shaped piece in the centre. The outside boards were spiked down to the cross-bearers. The vertical supports and the frames for the lockers were all made from old thwarts cut into 2 in. square pieces.

It is worth mentioning that when we wanted structural strength we used oak (for frames) and tough pine (for stringers); but we used up softwood when the timber merely had to provide a framework on which to fasten

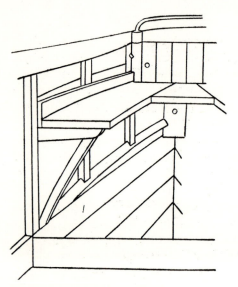

Fig. 57 Cockpit bench, side deck
vertical frames, stern locker and
cockpit floorboards

cupboard shelves or doors. The forward half of the cockpit had new soft-wood flooring. The cockpit benches were made from old thwarts which had to be cut to follow the curve of the boat. They were supported by built-in legs at the forward end and by a cross-bearer at the after end where they almost touch; so we put in a filling piece and made a 15 in. seat across the after end of the cockpit.

Cockpit lockers
The cockpit lockers were the next job. We made a large locker at the stern for paint, paraffin, and the like. Behind the benches were open lockers with a 2 in. coaming. These lockers all had slatted shelves of $\frac{1}{4}$ in. deal. In the forward part of the cockpit on the starboard side were the food lockers. The meat locker had a door framed in deal and panelled with perforated zinc. The other food locker was 13 in. wide, large enough to take a large dinner plate and the Sunday joint. There were two shelves, the bottom shelf being 7 in. above the cockpit floor level. It had double doors, framed in 2 in. by 1 in. white wood, panelled with ply, and hinged with small brass hinges. On the port side there was a large sail locker with a tongue-and-groove front that lifted out. It was one of the old locker fronts in the lifeboat. The sail locker cupboard also had two slatted shelves.

The bulwark rail

The stanchions or false timbers ran alongside the real timbers for about three planks and were fastened with copper nails and rooves to each plank. Those fore and aft had to be bevelled from the outside to prevent the bulwarks flaring outwards. They all projected about 7 in. above the capping and were spaced at every fourth timber; the first one was at the eighth timber from the stem and the last at the tenth from the stern. We clamped a long spline into position to find the sheer of the rail; it started about 2 in. high aft and swept through to a maximum height of $4\frac{3}{4}$ in., decreasing forward to about $2\frac{1}{2}$ in. We managed to get the bulwarks out of a 6 in. plank of BC pine 18 ft long and $\frac{3}{4}$ in. thick.

Before the bulwarks could be fitted the old capping which held the rowlock plates had to be ripped out and replaced by a new capping cut from some of the old red pine flooring. We cut slots in the capping to fit round each bulwark stanchion. The bulwark plank was fastened to the timbers by copper nails and rooves; and the tops of the timbers were cut off flush with the top of the plank. We then capped it with an oak rail, $\frac{3}{4}$ in. by 2 in. At either end it finished in a sharp concave sweep. The rail was screwed down to the bulwark plank with 2 in. screws. We cut three slots in the bulwarks amidships as scuppers. At this point the canvas covering the decks would have to finish under the old capping rail. Aft and forward, where the deck dropped below the level of the original rail, the canvas was fastened down with $\frac{3}{4}$ in. oak quadrants.

The bulwark rail greatly improved the appearance of the boat and gave one a real feeling of security when walking along the side decks, but I doubt if it was worth the time and the labour that it involved.

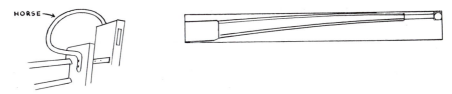

Fig. 58 Horse for a whaler or lifeboat, fastened to the sternpost. This is not suitable for larger craft, because of the inadequacy of the fastenings. The tiller can be cut to shape, as in the diagram; or it can be steamed and bent; or it can be laminated

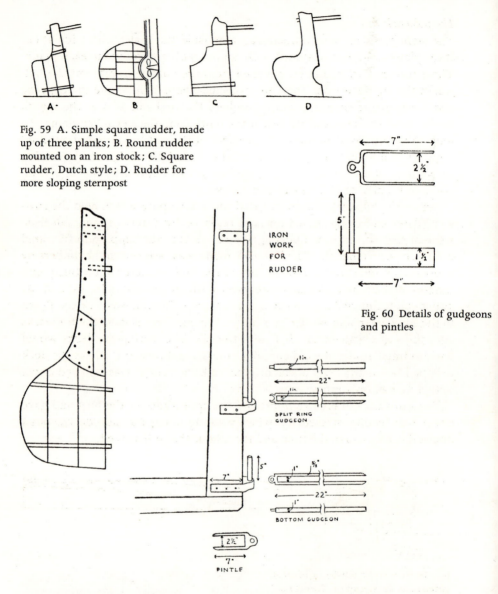

Fig. 59 A. Simple square rudder, made
up of three planks; B. Round rudder
mounted on an iron stock; C. Square
rudder, Dutch style; D. Rudder for
more sloping sternpost

IRON
WORK
FOR
RUDDER

Fig. 60 Details of gudgeons
and pintles

Fig. 61 Rudder, showing method of
construction and fastening. Top
gudgeon is fitted inside cheek pieces.
Details of gudgeons and pintles on
rudder and dimensions of their
ironwork. The upper drawing shows
two views of the bottom pintle. Wood
mock-ups are usually made and from
these the foundry can cast in iron or
bronze.

The rudder
The rudder originally fitted on a lifeboat is of little use for a sailing cruiser. It is too lightly built and much too small in the blade. The rudder of a 26 ft boat should be at least 1 in. thick. We made ours by pinning three 9 in. by 1 in. oak planks together with dowels and marking out the shape of the rudder on them. There are various shapes that might suit a 26 ft lifeboat. A rudder with a cut away trailing edge would look best with a raking stern-post, but as most lifeboats have a nearly vertical sternpost something like A, B or C would be best. The cheek pieces of the same weight of timber are riveted in place. The ironwork is $1\frac{1}{4}$ in. strap-iron drilled and bent to shape before being galvanised and riveted on. It will have to be made by a foundry or an engineering works.

Lifeboats often have an iron rod running vertically down the upper two-thirds of the sternpost, from which the rudder hangs by one split gudgeon and one ring that slips over the top. This will not be strong enough for the much heavier rudder that you are building, so in addition to these two fastenings fit a proper pintle at the foot with a spike of at least 5 in. and a corresponding gudgeon to slip over it.

These fittings can be nailed and rooved, or through-bolted, or both. You can buy them ready made from yacht chandlers, but they rarely fit. It is better to have them made up by a blacksmith.

Canvasing the deck and the cabin top
We rubbed down the deck and the cabin top with sandpaper, and then primed them with red lead and filled all the screw holes with putty. (When puttying holes, always brush in some wet paint first, then press the putty home and clean it off to a flat surface.)

Our canvas was 38 in. wide, so we had to sew two pieces together with a flat seam to make a piece large enough to cover the cabin top. This can be done on an ordinary sewing machine, but you will need a thicker needle than the usual one. The canvas then has to be cut to fit the cabin top, allowing enough to go over the edges of the cabin top and under the quarter-round battens that are to hold it in position. When the battens have been pinned on, the projecting canvas can be trimmed off with a very sharp knife or a broad, sharp chisel. The canvas on the foredeck did not stretch right across but was fitted to the edge of the king plank, which projected $\frac{3}{4}$ in. above the decking. We also used quarter-round battens here and round the edge of the bulwarks.

In laying the canvas on the cabin top it is best to do one side at a time.

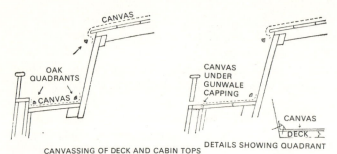

CANVASSING OF DECK AND CABIN TOPS

DETAILS SHOWING QUADRANT

Fig. 62 The canvasing of cabin top and decks, showing details of fastening

First paint the centre strakes with a good sticky paint (any old enamel you may have, or old flatting mixed with varnish). Then lay the canvas down so that the seam is in the middle, stretch it tightly fore and aft, and pin it down with a light batten. This is only a temporary fastening. Throw the canvas back leaving one side of the cabin roof clear, which you may then paint with the same sticky mixture. When it is tacky, pull the canvas over and smooth it outwards from the centre until it fits snugly. Pin it to the cabin sides with copper tacks at 18 in. intervals. Then fit the quarter-round batten underneath. Drill it and nail it into position with copper nails. You may now remove the temporary tacks. Repeat this process on the other side.

When the canvas was laid, I gave it two coats of priming, much diluted with linseed oil. To make it spread easily I worked with two brushes and two cans. One can was of paint, the other of water; I would wet a patch about 18 in. square, then I would paint it – and so on. It is an effective way of doing it, and is the usual custom in the Navy. After the second coat, which was applied without water, I gave it a coat of flatting and a top coat.

When we had to joint two pieces of canvas on the side decks, we overlapped them by about 3 in., turned the edge of the top piece under, and tacked it down with two rows of wide-head copper tacks.

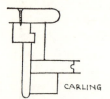

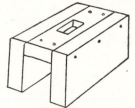

Fig. 63 *Left*: the construction of the sliding hatch. Running surfaces should be of brass strip   *Right*: the mast step, to fit over keelson

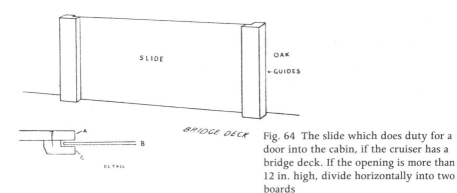

SLIDE

OAK

←GUIDES

A

B

C

BRIDGE DECK

DETAIL

Fig. 64 The slide which does duty for a door into the cabin, if the cruiser has a bridge deck. If the opening is more than 12 in. high, divide horizontally into two boards

Slides and hatches

As we had a full-length door to the cockpit we did not need a sliding hatch. From subsequent experience, I have drawn a bridge-deck into the plans, and with this one must have a sliding hatch. This may look to be rather a complicated bit of joinery, but provided it is constructed carefully, each operation is quite simple. There are more ways than one of making a sliding hatch. A simple effective and leakproof hatch is shown as in Fig. 63. The flat top is not as pleasing as a rounded hatch cover, which would be made up on bent frames and covered in ply or tongue-and-groove western red cedar (an easy wood to work). The slides would follow the same construction as shown here and they should taper downwards.

Louvres add greatly to the appearance of the varnished slides in a companionway and provide excellent ventilation.

Rubbing strakes

Lifeboats often have a top strake of mahogany below which is an oak rubbing strake of rounded section. If they are not too damaged, they can be rubbed down and varnished.

To match the rubber at the bottom of this strake, we put a half-round along the top, covering the join between the capping and the coaming. It was the same size of half-round as we used for the inside of the cabin top, and it improved the appearance of the boat a great deal. In the final painting it is worth treating these upper strakes in a different manner from the rest of the topsides.

Colour scheme

After much discussion we decided on our colour scheme, which was a sort of sugar-bag blue for the topsides, with a white boot and a black bottom. The top strake was painted a terra-cotta red; the rubbers a light blue; the bulwark capping rail was varnished oak; and the bulwarks were painted the same colour as the topsides. The cabin sides and bulkheads were terra-cotta; the decks and cabin top a cold stone. The king plank, the insides of the bulwarks, the bitts and the fife rail were terra-cotta. It suited her well.

Mildew proofing, or tanning
Most sail makers do a colourless mildew proofing, which has proved satisfactory over a number of years, but the sails must be kept dry and covered with this preparation, and it is necessary to reproof after two or three seasons. The alternatives are cutch tan, or linseed oil and ochre dressing, the former being a good preparation, although it tends to turn out a bit patchy and to fade rather, whilst the latter tends to stiffen the sails, and our sail makers did not recommend it, unless it was a question of having to leave the sails wet and uncovered on the spars. We used our sails untreated for one season and then had them cutch tanned. See page 57.

Ground tackle
Our 26 ft lifeboat had a bower anchor of 31 lbs and 15 fathoms of $\frac{5}{16}$ in. galvanised iron chain. This was enough to hold her in our shoal water and muddy bottom, whatever the conditions might be. But if you are likely to have to anchor in deeper water you should increase your chain to 25 fathoms. Our kedge anchor weighed 21 lbs. They were both long-shanked fisherman's anchors, excellent for holding but infernally awkward for stowing, unless you took the stock out and folded them flat. This is impracticable, as we found to our cost; for the pin has a habit of coming adrift, and has to be tied in position. If you are sailing single handed and have to anchor in a hurry you may well not have time to mouse the pin. Alternatives to the fisherman's anchor are the CQR and the Danforth. The CQR is a good anchor for holding in mud or sand, but not so good in shingle; shaped like a ploughshare, it does not need to be so heavy as an ordinary anchor; it can be stowed quite neatly on special galvanised iron chocks. One of these is fitted with a ring-bolt to take a lashing. These chocks are supplied by the manufacturers of this excellent anchor.

The cabin
The cabin of a cruising boat can either be a dank, dark hole, full of sails, gear, cooking utensils, bilgewater and mustiness, or a pleasant, homely little room, warm, snug, clean, tidy and dry.

To make sure it is dry, the decks must not leak, the opening ports must have proper washers, and the floorboards must be high enough to let the bilgewater slop about without wetting the floor. The cabin sides must be lined for one foot above the bunks, so that bedclothes don't get damp with the moisture that collects on the inside of the planking. (It is very important to ensure that there is proper ventilation behind the lining. This can be done by drilling 1 in. holes at 6 in. intervals along the top and bottom of the lining.)

If you are going to cruise in comfort it is essential to have a place for everything – literally everything. Then there is the business of cooking and washing up. One seems to be using a frying pan all the time, and frying is a messy business. The grease splutters and flies about, making the galley cupboard a very noisome hole after only a few meals. It is most important to design your galley so that grease and fat are confined within it, on a surface you can wipe easily.

In my present boat I have a two-burner Primus stove, which is highly efficient. This can either be mounted in gimbals if you are intending serious deep-sea cruising, or screwed down, or mounted in slides. Slides mean that the stove can be pushed back under the side decks when not in use and pulled forward when needed. Fiddles are an absolute necessity for cooking when under way. Both the Swedish Primus stove and Taylor paraffin stoves are fitted with these. The Swedish Primus which I use does have the advantage of having self-pricking burners. These can, I believe, be fitted to British makes at an extra cost. For washing up in my present boat I use a stainless steel operating theatre bowl, which can be bought from any hospital supply store. This drops into a circular hole cut in the Warite covered galley top. It looks very smart, is easy to keep clean, and is out of the way when cooking, as the stove slides over it. If one has water tanks under the bunks, water can be piped up to a small pump, such as a sunk-plunger, as made by Munster Simms, or a flipper type.

Under this washing bowl is either the foot of the port bunk or a locker, with access through the basin opening; to the left is another locker with a lift-up lid. Both these lockers are far better than those with vertical doors, for nothing can fall out and everything is to hand and can be seen without having to reach in up to one's shoulder, whilst knocking over tins of treacle and pots of marmalade. Both these lockers have slatted bottoms for ventilation. The plates are held in a conventional boat plate rack. As the bulkhead forward of the galley rises only about 9 in. above the galley level, there is a removable splashboard covered in Warite that fits in between bulkhead and stove to catch any flying fat.

Bunks

With the galley complete, we can turn to the bunks. They may be simple folding cots of canvas stretched across a metal framework or on a strong wooden pole; or they may be built up with a proper framework and a slatted top, in which case you will need a mattress. The most satisfactory is foam rubber. We made our bunks 6 ft 2 in. long (this is the minimum) by 2 ft 6 in. wide at the head and 2 ft 2 in. at the foot. They were 11 in. high from the floorboards.

If you use foam rubber or an internally sprung mattress it is better to make your bunk almost flat. The top of the bunks in my boat overlapped the floorboards by 3 in., the projecting ledge being supported by three galvanised angle-irons. This made the floor space 6 in. wider. If you decide to use a foam rubber mattress it is far cheaper just to buy the rubber mattress and make the cover for it yourself. We covered ours with strong mattress ticking, making the whole cover up, and just leaving the end and part of one side open to slide the rubber mattress in. I have never slept on anything more comfortable.

Alternatives are inflatable mattresses such as the Lilo, or polyvinyl covered kapok mattresses. These last had better be made in two or three separate sections, as otherwise they are very unwieldy. Internally sprung mattresses are probably too expensive for most small boat owners and anyhow they get damp and are liable to rust. Ordinary hair mattresses are quite unsuitable, for they are bound to hold the damp.

Cupboards

If you have room, it is useful to have a clothes cupboard in a small cruiser. Clothes we are not wearing we keep in waterproof (ex-US Army) kit bags, or suitcases which stow in the foc's'le or we hang them up on clothes hangers inside polythene covers. You do need a dry food cupboard in the cabin; you need a place for crockery, and some place for pots and pans and the indispensable kettle. We built our food cupboard just inside the door on the opposite side of the cabin under the side deck and projecting about 6 in. It had two shelves and a door, and on the top there was a polished oak ledge with a rail of half-round beading to prevent things from sliding off.

Windows and ports

Ports can be bought from any yacht chandler. We salved six from an old smack. These were of heavy brass, and cleaned up well. It is advisable to coat them with vaseline or varnish them as soon as they have been polished.

But even so they are an infernal nuisance to keep clean, so perhaps it is best to paint them. Our old ports leaked badly until we had removed the old perished washers and replaced them with $\frac{1}{4}$ in. strip rubber stuck into position with Bostik. Arrange the washer with the joint at the top, to avoid leaks. Opening ports are far more expensive than closed ones.

Deadlights
We fitted two 6 in. deadlights into the foredeck, and they turned the foc's'le from a dark and gloomy hole into a light and cheerful place, with room for at least one person to sleep and plenty of storage space.

Ventilators
There was a mushroom ventilator over the after end of the cabin above the galley, and another over the foc's'le on the starboard side. These ventilators will let in a good stream of air when fully open; and when they are screwed right down they will not leak, nor will they obstruct the sheets and lines.

The foc's'le
A 26 ft lifeboat has room for two folding cots up forward and a WC, but I think it is better to put in only the starboard one, and leave the port side for sail racks and stowage space. Sails are best stowed in netted racks, rather like the ones in railway carriages, but not so stoutly built. It is a good idea to have a slatted rack for kit bags at about bunk level on the port side forward of the cabin bulkhead, for it will keep them dry if bilgewater starts slopping over the floorboards, as may well happen if it comes on to blow.

Folding cots
The canvas of which they are made must be strong and heavy. It is laced on the outside to a stout pole (2 in. diameter), and on the inside to a stringer. The pole sits in two U supports fastened to the cabin bunks at one end and to the chain locker at the other. The bunk folds up against the cabin side when not in use and the pole is suspended in two cord loops. These bunks are very comfortable, but they are apt to be cold, so put two layers of blanket under you. You can fold all the bedding up inside them, which makes them neat and tidy when stowed in the daytime.

Heads – see page 272.

Chain locker
Our chain locker was up in the bows, the chain being tied to a heavy plate

on the keelson which had been part of the original lifting tackle on the life-boat. We made a small triangular platform of 1 in. by $\frac{1}{2}$ in. white wood which fitted in the bows about 4 in. above the keelson. The chain came up through the middle of the platform and rested on the $\frac{1}{4}$ in. slats with which it was planked. The remaining small scope led up through the hawsepipe to the anchor on deck. The hawsepipe was set in the king plank about 2 ft aft of the stem. It is a standard fitting with a flap that closes when not in use. You can buy them from any chandler.

In a smaller boat it would probably be better to make your chain locker of a rectangular box with a slatted bottom for drainage, and to put it just forward of the mast. The slats should not be more than $\frac{1}{8}$ in. apart or the links of the chain may get jammed in them. Twenty fathoms of $\frac{1}{4}$ in. chain weigh a lot, and it will improve the trim if you can bring that weight nearer the middle of the boat. We put our chain locker up forward because we wanted as much room as possible for bunks and stowage.

Ballast
We stowed our 8 cwt of ballast between the forward bulkhead of the cabin and the middle of the cockpit. With her usual crew of two or three people in the cockpit she trims well and is easy on the helm.

Sailing
She handles well under jib and mizzen, and if there is any weight in the wind we usually get under way with this rig. Our working jib is a small sail set half way out on the bowsprit, for we found that with a large headsail she was lightheaded when going to windward and would not come about easily. We keep the large headsail for light airs and for reaching and running. With her long straight keel she is slow in stays, but she never fails to come about if the jib is backed and the mizzen sheeted really hard in. A ketch of this kind is very easy to handle and is more manoeuvrable than a cutter or a sloop. Moreover you can lower the mainsail in a moment if it comes on to blow; you can then reef and reset it at leisure. For, without some mainsail set, the boat will not have much power, tacking or reaching. We reefed with reef points and permanent lanyards on the leech. We found that in heavy winds another 700 lbs of ballast would have enabled her to keep her way on, and not pay off when coming about.

As our bower anchor weighed 31 lbs, when there were 15 fathoms of cable out it was a brute to get up. The bottom of Harwich and Ipswich rivers and the Walton backwaters, where we did much of our sailing, is a heavy clayish mud, into which the bower bit with such a determined affection that it often needed two strong men to break it out. The trouble went on until we fitted a trip-line to the head, which made it much easier to break out the anchor. The trip-line was buoyed, so it was also a safeguard in case we might have to slip the anchor. Our kedge, a 21 lb fisherman's anchor on a 30 fathom hemp warp, was a good little anchor and never failed to bite.

The ketch was a nice easy boat to sail, stiff and sturdy and never heeling at much of an angle. Her best points were running and reaching and she was an excellent sea boat—as well she should be—being light and buoyant and dry as a bone. She was at her worst, as I suppose are all craft of this kind, when punching into a bit of a lop. Then one had to sail her full and free and keep her moving as hard as she would go. It was then that we felt the need of extra ballast.

Our first sail was on a day of light winds with fitful squalls. To begin with she seemed a large boat to handle, but we soon found that there was plenty of time to do everything. She never missed stays, but carried her way in a majestic arc. Even when moving with little way on, if we backed the jib and held the mizzen amidships she would always come round.

We sailed her two seasons without an auxiliary, but for comfort and peace of mind one must have a motor. On many of the East Coast estuaries the tide runs at 4 to 5 knots, and if the wind is foul one needs a very powerful or very well designed craft to stem it. The lifeboat ketch could not be expected to do so without an auxiliary.

Lifeboat Specifications
The cubic capacity for a 26 ft boat is 405 cu. ft and for an 18 ft boat is 162 cu. ft. The scantlings are as follows:

ITEM	MATERIAL	26 FT	18 FT
Keel	American elm, teak, oak or Australian spotted gum. Full thickness from stem to stern	$5\frac{1}{2}$ in. $\times$ $2\frac{3}{4}$ in.	4 in. $\times$ $2\frac{1}{2}$ in.
Stempost	British oak, teak, American elm or Australian spotted gum	$4\frac{3}{4}$ in. $\times$ $2\frac{3}{4}$ in.	4 in. $\times$ 2 in.
Sternpost	British oak, teak, American elm or Australian spotted gum	7 in. $\times$ $2\frac{3}{4}$ in.	6 in. $\times$ $2\frac{1}{4}$ in.
Hog piece	Teak, oak or Australian spotted gum	$5\frac{1}{4}$ in. $\times$ $1\frac{1}{8}$ in.	$4\frac{3}{4}$ in. $\times$ 1 in.

Lifeboat Specifications

ITEM	MATERIAL	26 FT	18 FT
Planking	Yellow pine, larch or Kauri pine	$\frac{5}{8}$ in.	$\frac{5}{8}$ in.
	Landings and butts as worked to be coated with good oil paint		
	Inside of planking to have one good coat of paint before working timbers		
Gunwales	American elm, teak, oak or ash	$\frac{7}{8}$ in. $3\frac{1}{2}$ in. (box)	2 in. $\times$ $1\frac{3}{4}$ in. (solid)
Sheerstrake	Mahogany, teak or elm	$\frac{3}{4}$ in.	$\frac{3}{4}$ in.
Timbers	American elm, ash or oak	$1\frac{3}{4}$ in. $\times \frac{7}{8}$ in.	$1\frac{1}{8}$ in. $\times \frac{3}{4}$ in.
Aprons	Oak, teak or ash, moulded at head	3 in.	$2\frac{1}{4}$ in.
Deadwood	Oak or ash (the moulding at throat to be not less than depth of keel + 1 in., the siding to be enough to give a surface of 3 in. apart from the rabbet)		
Keelson	Oak, teak, Oregon pine, pitch pine or Douglas fir	$4\frac{3}{4}$ in. $\times$ 3 in.	$3\frac{1}{2}$ in. $\times 2\frac{3}{4}$ in.
Thwarts	Teak, oak, red or pitch pine, larch, Douglas fir or other imported fir	No. 6 $9\frac{1}{2}$ in. $\times 1\frac{1}{2}$ in.	No. 4 8 in. $\times 1\frac{1}{4}$ in.
Gang-boards	To be of same dimensions and materials as thwarts		
Side benches	Yellow, red, or pitch pine, teak, larch, silver spruce, Douglas fir or other imported fir	1 in.	1 in.
Thwart knees	Oak, grown to form, siding	$1\frac{3}{4}$ in. (double)	$1\frac{3}{4}$ in. (single)
	Iron, wrought or stamped, siding	$1\frac{1}{4}$ in. (double)	$1\frac{1}{4}$ in. (single)
Rubbers	American elm, oak, teak, or ash	$1\frac{1}{2}$ in. $\times 1\frac{1}{4}$ in.	$1\frac{1}{4}$ in. $\times 1\frac{1}{4}$ in.
Risings	American elm, oak, teak, larch, or pitch pine	$3\frac{1}{2}$ in. $\times$ 1 in.	3 in. $\times$ 1 in.
Bilge stringers	American elm, teak, larch, or pitch pine	3 in. $\times \frac{3}{4}$ in.	3 in. $\times \frac{3}{4}$ in.

The conversion of a 26 ft lifeboat to a ketch-rigged cruiser

Lifeboat Specifications

ITEM	MATERIAL	26 FT	18 FT
Bottom boards	Teak, elm, larch, silver spruce, Douglas fir or other imported fir	$\frac{5}{8}$ in.	$\frac{5}{8}$ in.
Transoms	English elm or teak		$1\frac{1}{4}$ in.
	*If not in one piece (as for 18 ft boat) to be rabbeted and well secured. Fashion pieces should be worked to take in a row of plank end-fastenings		
Rudder	English elm, teak or mahogany –		
	thickness	$1\frac{1}{4}$ in.	1 in.
	cheek pieces	$\frac{3}{4}$ in.	$\frac{5}{8}$ in.
	Thickness in width to be maintained to level of top of keel		
Gauge of fastenings	Plank landings	12 s.w.g.	13 s.w.g.
	Stringers, hood ends, timbers, and garboards	10 s.w.g.	11 s.w.g.
	Risings and gunwales	8 s.w.g.	9 s.w.g.
	NOTE: All rooves to be of substantial section and not less than $\frac{3}{8}$ in. diameter by 18 s.w.g. for 13 s.w.g. fastenings, $\frac{1}{2}$ in. diameter × 18 s.w.g. for 12–10 s.w.g. fastenings, and $\frac{1}{2}$ in. diameter × 17 s.w.g. for 9–8 s.w.g. fastenings		
Ring-bolts	Wrought iron	$\frac{3}{4}$ in.	$\frac{1}{2}$ in.
Length of mast	Norway spar	16 ft	11 ft
Diameter of mast at clasp and head		4 in.–3 in.	3 in.–$2\frac{1}{2}$ in.

SIX

Converting a 27 ft lifeboat into a cutter

There is more than one solution to most design problems. A handsome conversion by a Dutchman was illustrated in *Yachting Monthly* in July 1960. *Sonnevaert*, as she is called, is a superbly professional job and is a real little ship – which is just what these conversions ought to be. It is a futile waste of time and money trying to make a lifeboat look like a modern yacht. They are far more in character with eighteenth and nineteenth century work-boats and little sailing ships. If you can keep this in mind you can make your boat so full of character that the owners of class yachts may well feel envious of you. This Dutch 27 ft lifeboat conversion, with its deep bul-warks, planked decks and loose-footed sails, more than bears this out. More than once I have had the pleasure of mooring alongside her in the

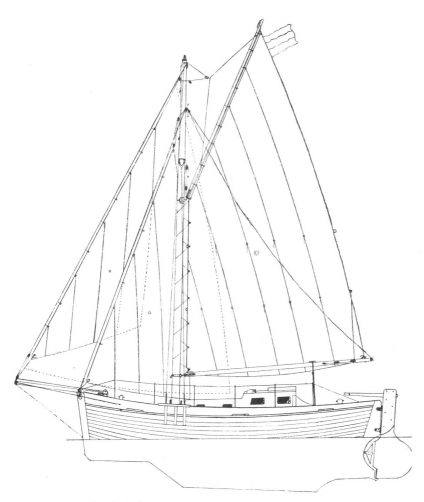

Fig. 65 Sail plan of 27 ft lifeboat
converted to a sloop

enchanting haven of her home port of Goes. She looked a thoroughbred.

This conversion of a 27 ft lifeboat was done some ten years after my 26 ft lifeboat ketch by Mr H. J. Van der Werff, to a design by C. Jansen. Apart from the rig, the main difference from the 26 ft lifeboat ketch *Grace Darling* lies in the smaller, stepped coach roof, the much higher bulwarks, and the ballast keel. The Dutch appear to have an unfailing eye for the lines of a boat, and *Sonnevaert* is no exception. She looks all of a piece, and has proved

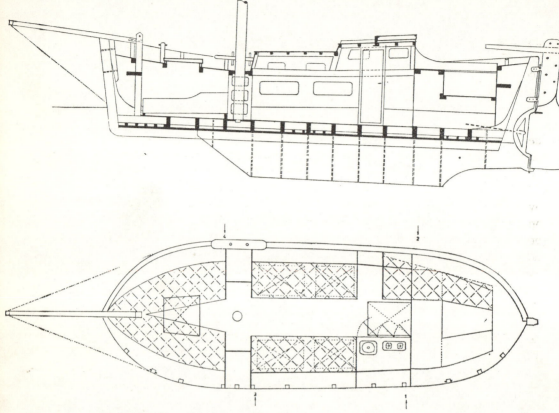

Fig. 66 Profile and accommodation plan
of 27 ft lifeboat

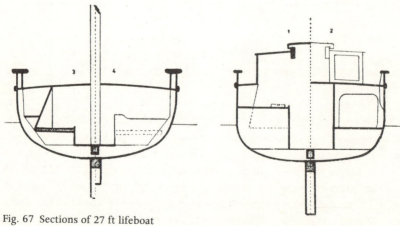

Fig. 67 Sections of 27 ft lifeboat

a great success. Her wide decks and deep bulwarks provide a safe play-ground for the owner's two little boys. Her cabin is light and roomy, and she is both sturdily and beautifully converted. Goes, in South Beveland, is a veritable home of conversions. I saw no less than seven converted lifeboats the last time I was there.

Sonnevaert has a 27 ft clinker-built hull, with a beam of 8 ft 4 in. She was designed for motor propulsion and has rather heavier scantlings than usual. She was built in Liverpool for a Finnish ship which ended her life in a ship-breaker's yard at Flushing.

The designer set himself quite a problem by planning a ballast keel of over 2,000 lbs. It certainly would not have been enough to hang this either on the keelson supported by floors, or on heavy floors. This particular problem was effciently solved by combining heavy deck beams and heavy floors, both reinforced and tied together with galvanised channel irons welded to the shape of the boat and bolted through beams, floors and planking. These steel frames were fitted both fore and aft of the mast. Comparable support was achieved at the after end of the cabin by a heavy bulkhead of $\frac{3}{8}$ in. marine plywood, screwed and bolted to a 4 in. by 4 in. deck beam and to a heavy floor and reaching out to the sides of the ship. The deck is heavily beamed and planked in $1\frac{1}{4}$ in. tongue-and-groove teak planking. This makes a very rigid hull, well able to withstand both the strains of the mast and rigging and the wringing strains if the ship dries out.

The ballast keel
This is delightfully simple. It consists of a box designed to fit over the existing keel; it was made up of $\frac{5}{16}$ in. steel plate, welded to shape. Ten $\frac{3}{4}$ in. keel bolts were welded in position, coming in through the bottom of the box. This was then filled with wet concrete and scrap-iron to exactly 3 in. from the top. (This was the depth of the existing wood keel.) The keel bolts were, of course, positioned to match the floors and the existing keel bolt holes. As soon as the keel had been cast it was offered up to the bottom of the boat. The points where the bolts touched the wood keel were marked and then drilled upwards. The wooden keel was well tarred and the entire boat dropped onto the keel assembly, the keel bolts pressing through the floors and keelson. The sides of the keel box are also drilled between the bolts so that transverse bolts can be fitted. This makes a very rigid structure and gives the lifeboat a draught of 4 ft 3 in.

It would be possible to cast a concrete keel straight onto the wooden keel. This would involve turning the boat upside down, drilling for the bolts, putting the bolts in position, then making up shuttering on each side of the existing keel. I have seen concrete keels successfully used on conversions and small craft in British Columbia, but these were for use on deep-water moorings and not for drying out. If carefully cast of Ciment fondu concrete and reinforced with $\frac{1}{4}$ in. steel rods, ballast keels can be constructed most simply by this method.

The other alternatives are to cast in lead, which is fairly simple. One makes up a box, as for the *Sonnevaert*'s box keel, but of wood with keel bolts in position; the lead is then heated in a cauldron and poured into the box. The only real difficulty is to find an adequate container for heating the lead.

For an iron keel, you make up a wooden pattern to the exact size of your ballast keel, drill the bolt holes and take it to a foundry. However, prices for foundry castings have increased so much over recent years that I would think that it might very well be cheaper to cast your keel in lead. And, of course, far cheaper in reinforced concrete.

Sonnevaert's steel-bound, concrete and iron keel weighed 2,200 lb. A shallow ballast keel 3 in. wide by 6 in. deep and say 20 ft long would weigh 1,150 lb if of iron; or 1,770 lb if of lead; and 310 lb if of solid concrete, or another 30 or 40 lb. if of reinforced concrete.

The rudder

The lifeboat's rudder was quite inadequate, so a $\frac{5}{16}$ in. steel plate was cut to shape, with its maximum area well down in the water. It is a large rudder and actually has 10 per cent of the lateral area of the hull. The rudderhead is made of teak in the same manner as is *Grace Darling*'s rudder.

The coachroof

This is framed in teak and covered in marine ply, with neat rectangular plate glass ports. The sliding hatch is of teak, and the companionway closes with teak slides. The forehatch is also of teak, with double coamings (to Maurice Griffiths's pattern). The high bulwarks are of iroko, steamed and bent to shape and fastened on false timbers. The stepped trunk is slightly more difficult to construct, but does give more headroom, without making the entire trunk look like a garden shed. This roomy hull has no less than five full-sized bunks; two in the forecastle, two in the cabin, and one quarter berth. Large cupboards are fitted behind each bunk.

The rig

The cutter rig follows Dutch practice in having a small loose footed and high-peaked gaff mainsail, a large staysail and a small jib. All the spars are solid and made from Oregon pine. Blocks are all suspended from grommets; the shrouds are supported by the hounds which consist of tapered hardwood pads. *Sonnevaert* has no runners, for the shrouds run well aft of the mast. The total sail area is relatively large: 430 sq. ft. She is comfortable, dry and, as the owner says, follows the motto of the sailors of Goes, which is "The slower the ship, the longer the pleasure." If this pleasure begins to pall, she has a Morris Vedette under her bridge deck, which in smooth water will push *Sonnevaert* along at the very respectable speed of 8 knots.

SEVEN

Conversions of 27 ft naval whalers into cruising ketches

British Naval whalers are 25 ft or 27 ft long with 6 ft of beam and a draught of 1 ft 8 in. with the centreboard up and 3 ft 9 in. with it right down.

Whalers are designed as yawls and their Montagu rig consists of a leg-of-mutton steering sail mounted on a small mizzen mast and a large standing lug on the main. There is also a fair-sized foresail. Neither mast is stayed, for they are sturdy spars, stepped on the keelson and through thwarts.

Rigged thus, the whaler is an interesting, lively boat to sail. The hull is very narrow, which, though convenient for pulling, limits the accommodation space in a conversion; but it is possible to make a very attractive and sporting sailing boat out of a whaler.

In a letter to *Yachting Monthly*, written nearly forty years ago, Mr A. S.

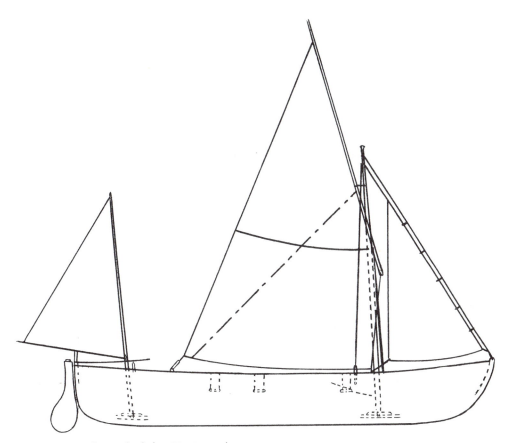

Fig. 68 27 ft Naval whaler, Montagu rig

Bennett described some of the virtues of his converted Montagu whaler. He said that the secret of a successful conversion lay in being content with the minimum headroom and having well distributed ballast, short masts and a maximum sail area of about 200 sq. ft. He goes on to describe how the whaler was used by the Navy for any 'dirty work' at sea. Though the whaler is lightly constructed, this lightness makes her easy to handle and her length enables her to ride the short steep estuary seas more comfortably than a shorter but deeper-keeled craft. Bennett quotes Mr C. E. Tyrell Lewis, who was, incidentally, one of the first to write about lifeboat conversions. Tyrell Lewis converted a whaler to a ketch, with a boomless mainsail, which, he said, would go to windward 'like a knife in a smart breeze' and would stay under her boomless mainsail alone.

I think that the boomless gaff mainsail is worth thinking about, for with it one could use brails. It does mean having rather a long gaff so that the leech of the sail is nearly vertical. It is possible in this case for the clew of the mainsail to overlap the mizzen mast but one would have to haul the clew round the mast when going on the other tack.

Whaler conversion 1. Centreboard ketch

Apart from altering the rig, strengthening the hull and decking in, this conversion involves the minimum of alterations. With the whaler's narrow hull, built-up topsides are of course, a necessity, for there is no room for side decks. It would very greatly improve both the appearance of the whaler and her accommodation if one raised the freeboard by at least one strake. This means raising the stem and sternposts by 9 in. and adding short false timbers to the timber heads running up to the new sheer. These false timbers should be fastened for at least two strakes down and clenched alongside each of the old timbers. Add a gunwale at the new sheer and screw the cabin sides to the inside of the new gunwale, which then acts as a carling. The cabin sides (of $\frac{1}{2}$ in. or $\frac{5}{8}$ in. mahogany or marine plywood) can be carried fore and aft beyond the cabin in a graceful sweep. This is not only decorative but also useful, for it provides extra freeboard where it is most needed. Cut small oblong windows in the cabin sides, or fit ports, and fasten a strong carling along the top to take the deck beams. The cabin top can have a 6 in. camber aft, decreasing to 3 in. forward. There should be a central sliding hatch in which the cook can stand when working at the galley, for the cabin head-room is only 4 ft 4 in. The cabin top and deck should have foot-rails on either side as there is no side deck to walk on.

There is a large hatch in the foredeck for access to the foc's'le and for the crew to stand in when tending the main halyards. The cockpit is separated from the main cabin by a bridge deck in which the unstayed mizzen mast is stepped. Whalers are not very sensitive to the fore and aft placing of the rig. In this conversion design I have rigged her as a jib-headed ketch. The mizzen mast carries a bermudan sail of 15 ft on the luff and 8 ft on the foot. The main mast is stayed from the head by one pair of shrouds and forestay leading inside the stemhead. To save windage at anchor, for simplicity in building and for safety in heavy weather, the main mast is a short spar carrying a vertical gunter rig. The shrouds and stays are eye-spliced over a shoulder just below the masthead. There is a sheave 6 in. below this for the main halyards. The jib halyards run through a block suspended just below the sheave. The mainsail is 9 ft 6 in. on the luff and 9 ft 6 in. on the foot.

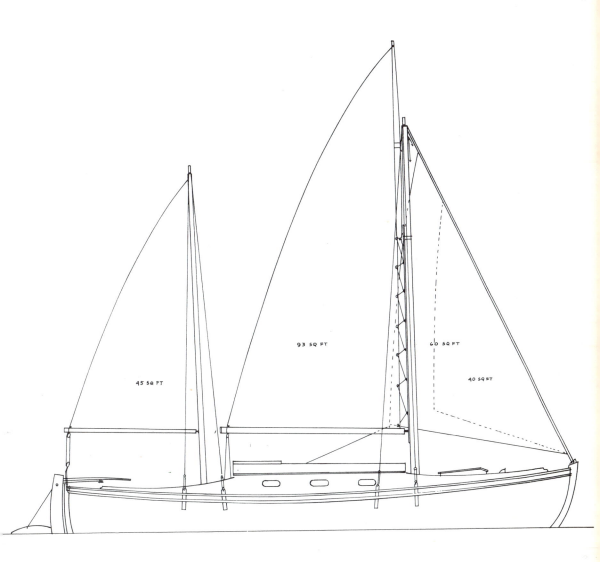

45 SQ FT

93 SQ FT

60 SQ FT

40 SQ FT

Fig. 69 Sail plan of 27 ft centreboard
whaler ketch

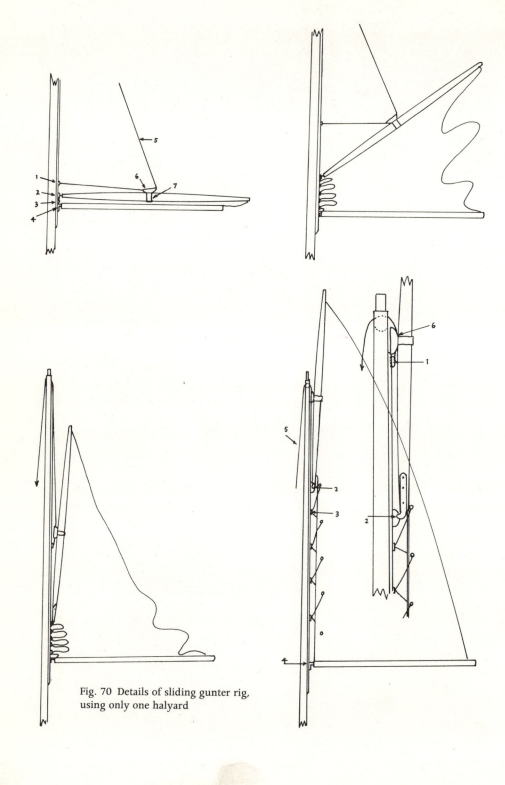

Fig. 70 Details of sliding gunter rig,
using only one halyard

The foresail is 17 ft on the luff and 9 ft on the foot. The foresail sheets will lead aft over rollers set on the shrouds. Wykeham-Martin furling gear would be most useful on a long narrow craft like this (see page 59). The mizzen is 13 ft on the luff and 7 ft in the foot.

The mizzen mast should be a stout spar $4\frac{1}{2}$ in. in diameter at the deck tapering to $2\frac{1}{2}$ in. at the head. If it is unstayed, as it could be, it can easily be unshipped to reduce windage. In my book *Small Boat Conversion*, Kenneth Gibbs described an effective vertical sliding gunter. It would certainly be a most suitable rig for this centreboard conversion. It has a single part wire and rope halyard, the luff being set up by bearing down on the sliding gooseneck. The sail can be fitted with either point or roller reefing, and when reefed to any position the yard remains close up to the mast.

A magazine, consisting of a short length of standard C-sectioned mast track, clips onto the mast below the main track and houses the gooseneck, yard slide, and slides to which the luff of the mainsail is laced, in one neat unit. This makes it possible to remove the sail complete with its yard and boom in a matter of seconds.

The sketches show how the rig works. In Fig. 70 the mainsail is stowed. Referring to the numbers: 1. A strong slide working in the mast track which extends from a few inches above the gooseneck to just below the halyard sheave. 2. Special jaws for the yard, also working in the track. 3. Slides to which the luff of the sail is laced. 4. Sliding gooseneck. 5. Main halyard. 6. Span shackle attached to yard by a band.

Except for 1, all the fittings that work in the mast track would at this stage be housed in the magazine and be held by a pin through the top of the magazine track.

Hauling on the halyard gradually raises the yard, and at the same time slide 1 works up the mast track until the position shown bottom right is reached. It will be noted that slide 1 is now hard up to the span shackle 6. The yard is now hauled up the mast as far as it will go, the halyard is belayed, and the luff set up by bearing down on the gooseneck 4 and locking it in position.

To reef, the gooseneck lock is slackened off, and the boom rolled *up* to the desired reef position, the halyard slackened away to lower the sail, belayed, and the gooseneck set up. The yard will keep its angle to the mast so long as there is tension on the halyard and luff of the sail.

To stow the sail, the halyard is cast off and the yard lowered down on the boom. The luff slides and yard jaw will settle into the magazine. The span shackle is cast off, the pin inserted in the magazine, and the whole thing

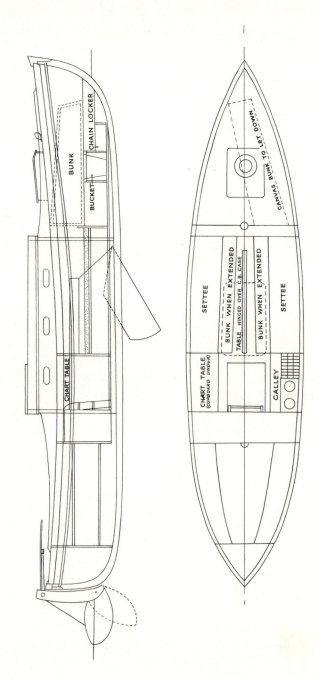

Fig. 71 Plan and elevation of 27 ft
centreboard whaler ketch

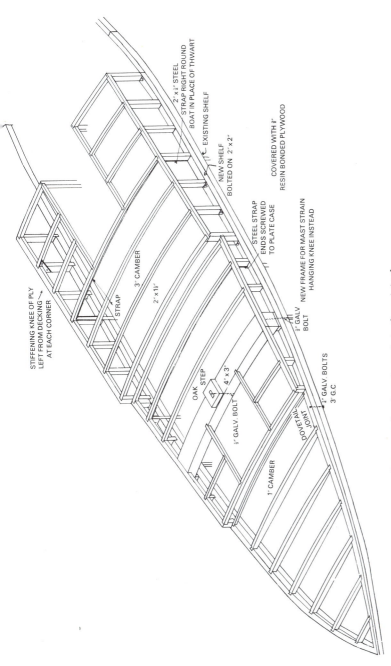

STIFFENING KNEE OF PLY
LEFT FROM DECKING →
AT EACH CORNER

STRAP

3" CAMBER

2" x 1½"

OAK

STEP

4" x 3"

½" GALV. BOLT

DOVETAIL
JOINT

½" GALV. BOLTS
3' G.C.

1" CAMBER

½" GALV
BOLT

NEW FRAME FOR MAST STRAIN
HANGING KNEE INSTEAD

STEEL STRAP
ENDS SCREWED
TO PLATE CASE

COVERED WITH ⅜"
RESIN BONDED PLYWOOD

NEW SHELF
BOLTED ON 2" x 2"

EXISTING SHELF

2" x ¼" STEEL
STRAP RIGHT ROUND
BOAT IN PLACE OF THWART

Fig. 72 Foredeck and cabin framing for the whaler conversion *Pintail*, designed and carried out by John Lee, ARICS, of Leigh-on-Sea. The decking was ⅜ in. marine ply and the steel straps were put in in three pieces, so that they could be slipped under the stringers. The beams and deck are lightly constructed, but with the steel straps and steel floor they are quite strong enough.
In this conversion the main mast is hollow, 27 ft long, and the boom is 12 ft. The mizzen is in the original place, stepped on the keel, and needs no runners. With only 100 lbs of ballast aboard she heels as far as the rubbing strake but no further. A ring is fastened into the end of the plate arm for a small tackle, so that it can be raised from the cockpit. *Pintail's* sail area of 280 sq. ft is as follows: foresail 60 sq. ft, main 190 sq. ft, mizzen 30 sq. ft

9 *Petrel*, 27 ft fin keel bermudan whaler
ketch on chocks (above) and laid over to
expose port side for fibreglassing

taken off the mast if you want to take the sails ashore.

It is a most efficient arrangement. The jib-headed mizzen should be set on a track.

The whaler-cruiser is a lively sporting craft and should be kept as such.

About 5 cwt of ballast should be kept as low in the boat as possible. The cabin arrangement is simple. In the plan I have put in two narrow benches to sit on and canvas cots which drop into position when required. During the day the bedclothes can be folded up in the canvas bunks, which will then make comfortable backrests. If there were full-width bunks there would be no foot room between the bunk risers and the centreboard case, which supports a folding table. The foot of the bunks projects into the foc's'le where there is a lavatory bucket under the forehatch. There is a chart table with a cupboard underneath it aft on the port side; the galley is on the the starboard side and has a half-bulkhead separating it from the cabin.

The bridge deck, with removable bulkhead panels, provides enough space for a cupboard for clothing or food. Alternatively, part of the bridge deck could open into the cockpit and be used to store warps, fenders and other boat's stores.

If there is to be no engine, you should have rowlocks on either side of the cockpit, and carry a pair of folding sweeps. Hinges for folding oars can be bought from yacht chandlers. Full length oars can be very difficult to stow.

Until I started on my previous book I had only once seen a whaler conversion. One summer's evening she came into Hamford Water, where we were moored. She moved gracefully through the water, turned about and was off again. There was no point in trying to chase her, for we were in the lifeboat ketch which, good boat though she was, had not got the heels of the whaler. A lifeboat is roomy, which obviously makes her convert well, but I must say that the whaler's sailing performance is most attractive. She is an out-and-out sailing craft, with the rather too small centreboard already built in. The conversion work, like that of any 'working' sailing boat, should be planned to interfere as little as possible with the boat's performance. This can be done with the centreboard whaler and should produce an excellent cruiser. She is, of course, both lively and somewhat tender and if maximum performance is wanted in any weight of wind, has to be sailed a little like a dinghy, with the crew sitting her out.

Whaler conversion 2. Fin keel ketch

There is more than one way of converting any boat, and Mr J. D. Rogers of Southampton has made a quite different version of the whaler conversion.

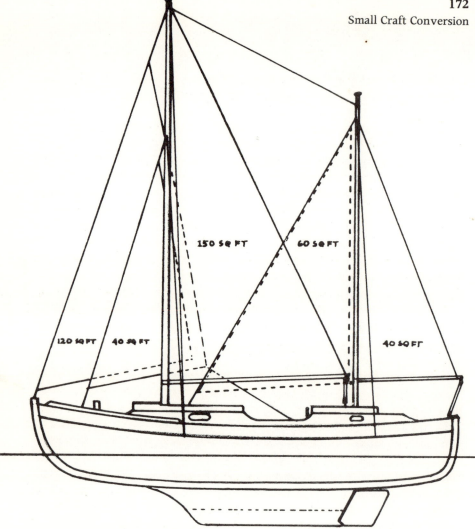

Fig. 73 Sail plan and elevation of fin-
keel whaler ketch, designed by
J. D. Rogers

This fine, seagoing boat is a bermudan ketch with cabins fore and aft and a
centre cockpit. The most interesting feature is the weighted fin keel which
replaces the centreboard. This is a proper fin keel, cast in two halves and
bolted to a plate that goes up through the centreboard box. The foot of the
new rudder is pivoted on the after end of the keel. This gives the whaler a
draught of 4 ft.

The cabin arrangement was chosen to give the maximum carrying space
and comfort coupled with seakindliness. By having cabins and decks at both

extremities of the ship, she was not likely to be pooped by a following sea and the extra two strakes would keep the cockpit dry.

She was intended for coastal cruising, and as one generally cruises by day and sleeps by night it naturally followed that the centre cockpit gave the easiest riding position. At night, when at anchor, the crew sleeps and worries little about the motion of the ship. The centre cockpit also made it easier to move about the ship. The galley stove is situated just inside the hatch in easy reach of anyone in the cockpit, or for serving directly to the cabin table. The bunk under the stove was for the cook, so that with the minimum of effort she (or he) could brew the morning tea. The cabins have 4 ft 6 in. headroom.

The conversion was started by making the ship as comfortable as possible within the limits of the whaler's hull; then she was rigged as a bermudan ketch. At the time no fin keel was fitted, the idea being to rely on the existing plate, but it was soon found that in a breeze of over Force 3 a trapeze had to be used when going to windward and the plate was too small to be effective. The length of her keel made her difficult in stays and it was inadequate as ballast.

The following winter a fin keel was fitted. It was completely successful; all the faults disappeared and she became a fine ship, not stiff enough in a blow to endanger the sails, but stable enough to give the crew peace of mind when she was blown down. With the ballast carried on the end of the fin it is most effective, and therefore requires less mass than would be needed if stowed inside the ship.

For normal working, in winds of over Force 4, 185 sq. ft of sail was sufficient. In lighter airs she was under-canvased. So, later on, a large jib was set on the foretopmast stay, which was quite adequate.

One day the fin keel whaler was knocked down to 45° during a squall when beating to windward with all sail set. She behaved admirably. One might have expected her to wallow, but instead she seemed to accelerate and smashed through half a dozen short seas, wetting her mainsail over the lower half.

A good use was made of the old centreboard box, by letting the fin keel plate fill the whole of it, thus spreading the strain over as great an area as possible. If the original whaler had had no centreboard box, many floors would have been spaced throughout the length of the keel. The fin was faired off with wood.

The cockpit was self draining with two side benches, and came over part of the centreboard box. There was plenty of storage space under the cockpit floor. The steering was by a teak wheel, with a chain and cable to the rudder yoke, and in emergencies a tiller could be fitted into the rudder post. The sternpost to support the rudder was welded onto the stern of the fin keel.

The cabins each had two spring berths, the forward berths extending under the cockpit floor for some 18 in. These two berths tended to become wet in a hard blow if the bilges were not dry, but with care this need not have happened, for there was 4 in. clearance between the hull and the bunks. Forward of the mast and under the hatch there was a bucket toilet. A pump WC could have been fitted, but the designer-converter was against it, for ships have been lost through a sticky or leaky valve when the pan is below the waterline.

A 6 ft dinghy was carried across the deck aft; made of ply, it weighed some 40 lbs. This dinghy could carry three adults, and went well with a 4 h.p. outboard on the transom. This outboard was also the ship's auxiliary. It was fitted onto a bracket on a single point of suspension, with a safety rope attached to the motor. This bracket resembled a transom sticking out of the side of the hull. It protected the motor from a lot of spray and water. What water did hit the transom was deflected by small breakwaters. If the seas were too big for these little breakwaters it was considered useless fitting an outboard on the bracket and expecting it to push the ship.

The reason why a standard side-mounting bracket was not used was because the motor had a short shaft for dinghy work. This arrangement is better because a long shaft on a dinghy can be dangerous and is awkward for beaching. All that showed on the hull when the motor and bracket were stowed away was an oak block.

The little bracket was raked for strength and although there were no pins to secure it, it was perfectly safe because the whole assembly held tight with its weight alone. With the weight and twist of the motor it was completely rigid. The only way to insert the bracket and withdraw it was for the weight to be completely taken off.

The breakwaters were battens screwed onto the forward side of the transom and were essential to prevent scooping up waves. In all but the roughest conditions they worked perfectly. After a couple of seasons an 8 h.p. Stuart Turner was installed, driving the ship through a quarter installation.

Generally speaking, the sail plan was a success, and sail could be set under practically any conditions. The small mainsail with its kicking strap was very efficient. The mast heights were 29 ft and 22 ft. Snags in the

10 Moulded bracket for quarter
installation on *Petrel*

11 Two halves of the ballast keel

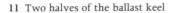

12 Ballast keel bolted to the steel plate
that goes up through the centreboard
case. Either side of plate is faired-off
timber. *Petrel*

13 Foredeck of *Petrel*

14 After cabin, showing how dinghy is stowed

15 Centre cockpit showing wheel steering and offset engine box

16 Internal rudder and steering arrangement

17 Pulpit

18 'Sternpost' on ballast keel. Space
between this and fore side of the rudder
is faired off with timber. *Petrel*

19 Stern view showing fin keel and
rudder in position on *Petrel*

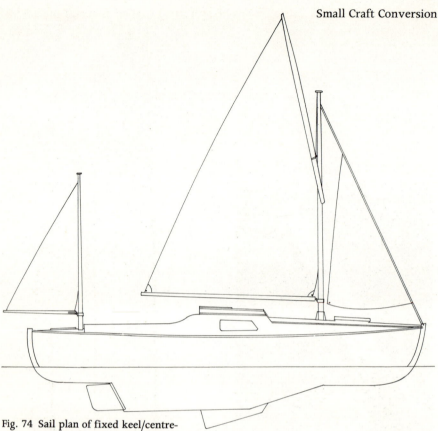

Fig. 74 Sail plan of fixed keel/centre-
board whaler designed by Richard F.
Day of Don Mills, Ontario

arrangement were the draughts which tended to blow into the after cabin
in the early hours of the morning, and the fact that although positive, like all
whalers she was slow in stays.

The addition of a ballasted keel does seem very worth while for any
whaler conversion. This whaler has cruised successfully down-Channel
without giving her crew any anxiety.

Whaler conversion 3. Centreboard fixed keel ketch

This centreboard ketch with the board working through a fixed keel has
been planned for sailing on the Great Lakes by Richard Day of Don Mills,
Ontario, Canada. The main difference from the two previous conversions
is the removal of the centreboard case and the addition of a ballast keel and
centreplate. The keel is made up of concrete cast between marine ply
shutters which are held in position by being bolted through the sides of

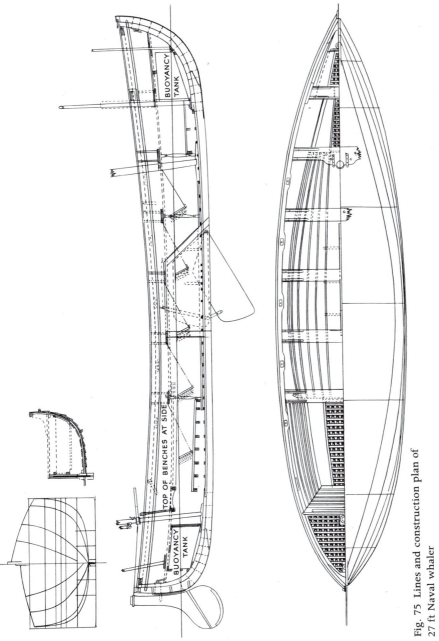

BUOYANCY TANK

TOP OF BENCHES AT SIDE

BUOYANCY TANK

Fig. 75 Lines and construction plan of
27 ft Naval whaler

the original keel. These shutters remain in position after the keel has been cast. The weight of the keel is supported by drift bolts fastened through the original keel to eight substantial floors.

The rudder post, as in the previous whaler conversion, comes well inside the ship's waterline. The steering arrangement consists of a galvanised pipe which houses the rudder post. The upper, open end of this pipe is well above the waterline. A tiller yoke is keyed and fastened to the rudder post with a nut-and-lock washer. The yoke is mounted in an up-and-down fashion instead of transversely. Nylon-covered wire rope cables are attached to each end of the yoke. These lead through sheaves fastened under the starboard cockpit bench (the motor well prevents them going round to port) and the cables go two and a half times round the wheel drum. The result is positive steering; that is, you turn the wheel in the direction in which you wish to go.

The deck in this whaler conversion is made up of $\frac{5}{8}$ in. marine plywood carried on 2 in. by 2 in. deck beams. The cabin sides are of $\frac{3}{4}$ in. marine plywood with the cabin trunk supported by a $\frac{3}{4}$ in. marine ply frame. The cabin sides are screwed to the gunwale, which acts as a carling. The whole assembly is further strengthened by drift bolts through the end grain of the cabin frame sides and gunwale. The bottom frame is joggled over a stringer and also clench-fastened to it. This should make a light but very strong cabin trunk.

Centreboard assembly

The old centreboard case has been taken out. The same pivot hole in the keel is used to support the original centreboard. The board is raised by a chain that runs up to a galvanised pipe rising to 16 in. above the keelson. The existing centreboard slot is closed by means of a shaped piece of oak 6 ft long, 8 in. wide and 4 in. thick. This runs the full length of the case and is rabbeted into it to the depth of 1 in. This, combined with the new floors, should compensate for the fore and aft stiffening effect of the old centreboard case.

As this hull had been thoroughly dried out, Mr Day cleaned the centreboard slot down to the bare wood and covered it with polyester resin. The same treatment was given to the 6 ft long filling piece, which was bedded in the polyester resin. Finally the whole assembly was covered with polyester and glassfibre mat to halfway out on the garboard strakes inside, and over the whole of the outside of the centreboard case, the ballast keel and finally the whole outside hull. She should be a very dry ship.

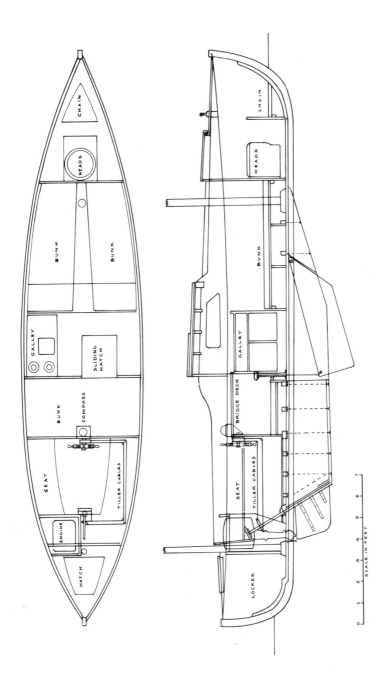

Fig. 76 Plan and elevation of Canadian fixed keel/centreboard whaler

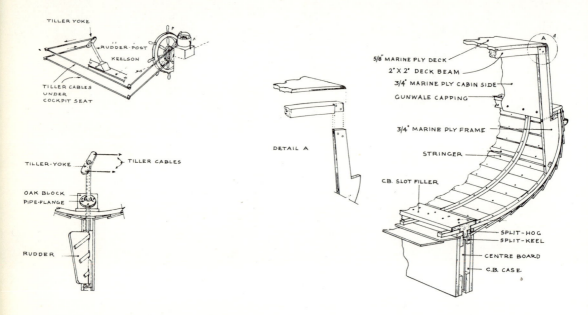

TILLER YOKE

RUDDER POST

KEELSON

TILLER CABLES
UNDER
COCKPIT SEAT

TILLER-YOKE

TILLER CABLES

OAK BLOCK

PIPE-FLANGE

RUDDER

DETAIL A

5/8" MARINE PLY DECK

2" X 2" DECK BEAM

3/4" MARINE PLY CABIN SIDE

GUNWALE CAPPING

3/4" MARINE PLY FRAME

STRINGER

C.B. SLOT FILLER

SPLIT-HOG

SPLIT-KEEL

CENTRE BOARD

C.B. CASE

Fig. 77 Cut away and detail drawings
by Richard Day of his fixed
keel/centreboard whaler

Fig. 78 Wheel steering gear

Fig. 79 Tiller yoke and rudder

Fig. 80 Framing of cabin top

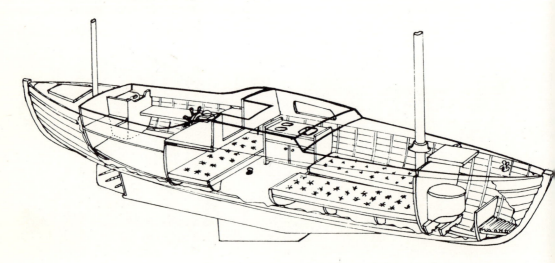

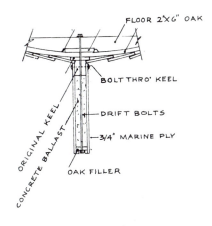

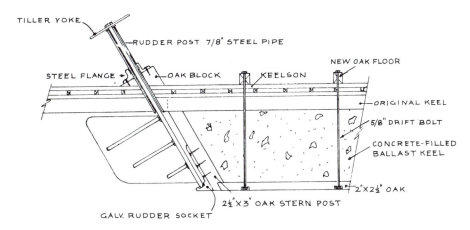

Fig. 81 Ballast keel

The power unit is a 7 h.p. outboard motor working through a shaft from a watertight motor well just astern of the rudder on the port side. The cabin has about 4 ft headroom, but a sliding hatch means that at least in fine weather the skipper can stand up straight to put on his trousers. In the cabin there are the normal port and starboard bunks but also one arranged across the boat at the after end of the cabin, tucked under the bridge deck. The heads, which consist of a chemical toilet, are in the fore-peak and are completely bulkheaded off from the cabin. In a cruising boat of this size this seems to me to be a good idea. Access, of course, is by the forehatch.

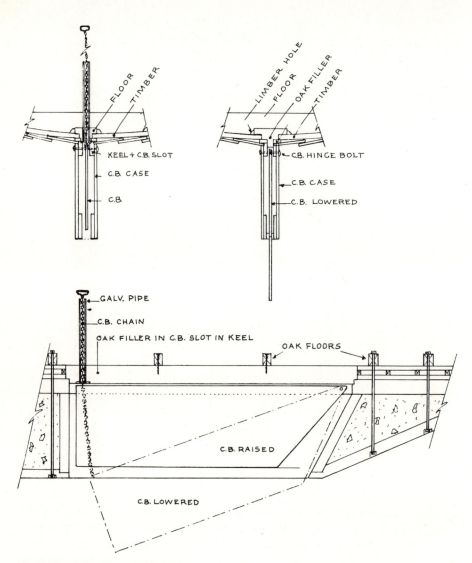

Fig. 82 Centreboard case and details of
fastenings

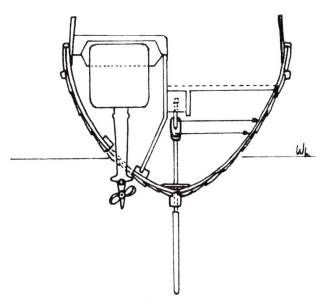

Fig. 83 Outboard motor well

The original Montagu or dipping lug, foresail and jib-headed mizzen have been retained, but the main has been fitted with a boom—a wise precaution, for the mainsheet block on a loose-footed mainsail, flogging about in a wind, can be a somewhat lethal companion.

A watertight outboard motor well fitted to a 27 ft whaler was once described in *Yachting Monthly*, by Mr C. Graham of Nigeria. A square casing of $\frac{3}{4}$ in. oak was built 8 in. across at the bottom and 10 in. at the top. It was riveted at the top to the after thwart and at the bottom to two pieces of oak 3 in. by 3 in. running fore and aft along the floor. A hole was cut in the hull planks so that the shaft of the engine could be lowered into the casing when required. The hole was arranged so that the garboard was not damaged, but the next two planks were cut through and screwed to the casing. A liberal supply of white lead was put in all the joints, and they never leaked.

This arrangement—the engine was only 3 h.p.—worked very well. When under sail, water was apt to slop up through the well, so a watertight hatch cover was made for it. The advantage of using an outboard in this manner is that it becomes virtually an inboard installation, but it can be removed when sailing, and can of course be taken ashore for winter storage.

EIGHT

Converting 26 ft and 27 ft lifeboats into motor-sailers, power cruisers and fishing boats

Twenty-six ft lifeboats of wood, glassfibre or steel can be converted into effective motor-sailers, power cruisers and inshore fishing boats. The larger 28 ft and 30 ft lifeboats are an even better proposition for such conversions. There are considerable differences in the requirements for a lifeboat conversion for use on the canals and for one fit to stand up to rough seas. The canal or inland waterway boat can have much more freeboard, providing she is not too top-heavy. The construction of decks, coach roofs, wheelhouses, etc. can be much lighter than those in a seagoing vessel. Her motor can be less powerful and steadying sails or auxiliary sails are not needed. A little ballast, say 500–600 lbs stowed under the floorboards, will make her that much steadier. In other words, the inland waterway craft

20 Motor lifeboat with built-up topsides showing ramp from foredeck down to gunwale

Fig. 84 Sail plan of 26 ft lifeboat motor cruiser

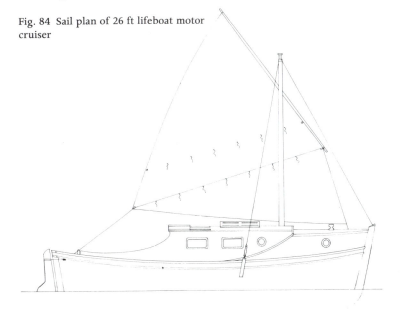

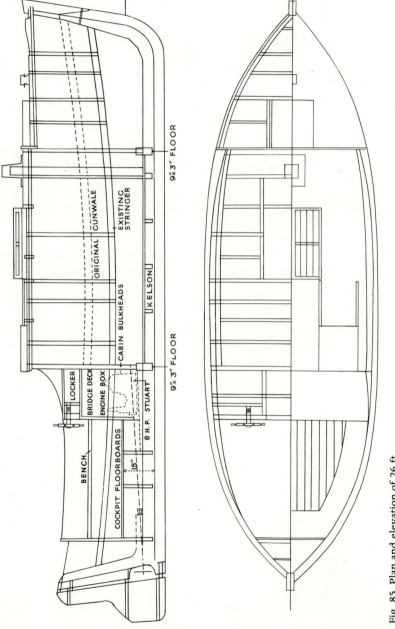

9" x 3" FLOOR

EXISTING STRINGER

ORIGINAL GUNWALE

KELSON

CABIN BULKHEADS

9" x 3" FLOOR

LOCKER

BRIDGE DECK

ENGINE BOX

8 H.P. STUART

BENCH

COCKPIT FLOORBOARDS

15"

Fig. 85 Plan and elevation of 26 ft lifeboat motor cruiser, showing construction

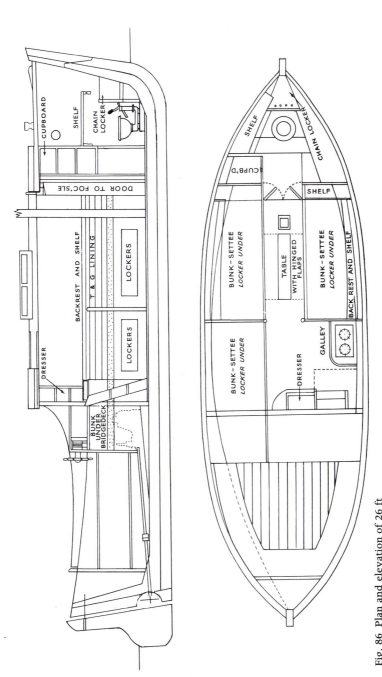

Fig. 86 Plan and elevation of 26 ft lifeboat motor cruiser showing accommodation

can be much nearer to a floating caravan, whereas the seagoing vessel has to be a proper ship, altogether more ruggedly constructed, with much less freeboard, more ballast, a more powerful motor installation and preferably with auxiliary sail.

For most power conversions it is necessary to raise the freeboard. To do this false stem and sternposts must be fitted, to support the additional topside planking and, in the case of the sternpost, to allow for the propeller gap.

The 26 ft clinker-built wooden lifeboat will make a good seagoing power cruiser, and the work is considerably easier than in converting to sail. There is no need for a false keel, but bilge keels are worth putting on, for they will improve her stability and make her sit up straight when aground.

The first of these designs for a lifeboat motor cruiser was worked out over twenty years ago. I think, however, that the addition of a wheelhouse, which also allows for standing headroom over the galley, is worth considering. It is a considerable refinement, but it adds to the complications of building.

Construction

A certain amount of additional stiffening of the hull will be provided by the bulkheads at either end of the main cabin. Floors should be fitted in the way of the bilge keels and should be fastened to fore and aft stringers, which should overlap the bilge keels by 8 in. at either end. As the stringers will be sitting on top of the timbers, put in filling pieces in the way of the bilge keel bolts. The bilge keels should not be less than 6 ft long, made of 3 in. oak or elm planks on edge, about 6–9 in. deep. They should be faced with $1\frac{1}{2}$ in. wide galvanised iron strip, $\frac{3}{8}$ in. thick. If the conversion is for use on

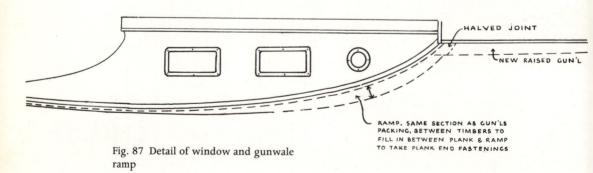

Fig. 87 Detail of window and gunwale ramp

canals there is no point in fitting these bilge keels, though heavy rubbing strakes are essential.

There will, of course, be additional floors in the way of the engine and acting as engine bearers. Engine installation has already been discussed. For seagoing purposes, a fairly hefty diesel is advisable with at least 15 h.p. For sheltered waters and for use on canals an 8 h.p. diesel or petrol engine would be quite adequate.

The first job is to raise the stempost by 12 in. and the sternpost by 6 in. Put in a substantial bulkhead framing at the after end of the foredeck and join it up to the stem with a new gunwale, as in the diagram; and then, by means of a curved ramp, lead the new gunwale back to the stern of the boat. Put in new timbers alongside the old ones 18 in. below the old gunwale, and fasten them through at least three strakes. The deck beams for the foredeck are next fitted. The ramp will have the same cross-section as the gunwale. Then planking should be cut to the required curve after fastening. The covering board or capping will cover the tops of the new timbers and the new top strake and will sweep up the ramp in a fair curve. The foredeck can be covered in $\frac{1}{2}$ in. marine ply. Take care when putting in the beams to leave enough space between them for the fore-hatch. The deck beams are checked into the new gunwale and fastened. The false

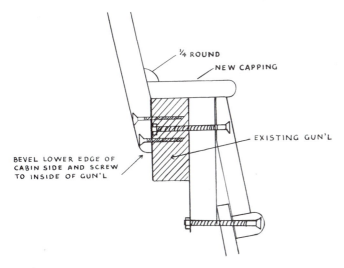

Fig. 88 Detail showing how cabin side
is fastened to original gunwale

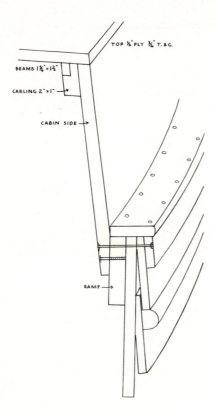

Fig. 89 Section of cabin side and
gunwale showing construction of ramp

stem- and sternposts should be scarphed into the old ones and through-
bolted. The planks of the new topsides can be clench-fastened onto this
framework. To get the shape of the planks right, lay the bottom one along
the old gunwale and mark in the curve on the lower side. Now measure the
width of the original planking amidships and at 3 ft intervals up to the stem.
You will find that it narrows considerably as it goes forward. Check this
width with the space to be filled by your new planking at its greatest depth,
and if necessary alter your measurements so that you fill the space with
planks of an even size. Mark the widths on your first plank, the bottom one,

and cut it to shape leaving an extra $\frac{3}{4}$ in. at the top edge to form the land for the next plank. Then clamp it into position and fasten with clenched nails to each timber, and to the plank below once between each timber. Mark up the next plank in the same way and so proceed. To make the planks lie close to the stempost, cut a rabbet in the new stempost and bevel the lands of each plank so that the planks come to a flush surface at the rabbet. When the fore part is planked you can cut off the protruding after ends of the planks. Alternatively, the whole thing could be cut from one wide plank of iroko or mahogany or from a sheet of $\frac{5}{16}$ in. marine ply. The capping should not be fitted until the cabin sides are in position.

The cabin is much simpler. The sides consist of a single wide plank of iroko or mahogany, $\frac{3}{4}$ in. by 2 ft 6 in., or a sheet of $\frac{5}{16}$ in. marine ply running

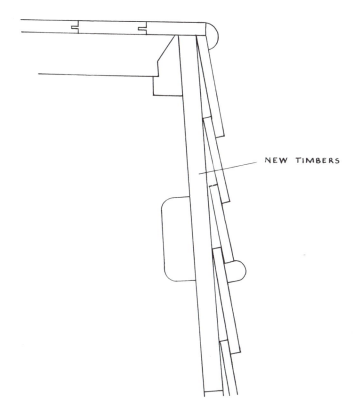

NEW TIMBERS

Fig. 90 Section of raised foredeck with clenched planks and short new timbers

aft in a long sweep to act as a coaming for the cockpit. The sides are fastened to the bulkheads fore and aft, and along the lower edge to the ramp, which acts as a carling. There is also a heavy carling along the top into which the deck beams are checked. This makes a strong and rigid structure. Plank the top with $\frac{3}{4}$ in. tongue-and-groove and cover it with canvas or cover with $\frac{1}{2}$ in. marine ply. The capping may now be put on the ramp.

The skylight

This not only gives you some light overhead, but also provides a full 6 ft of headroom. The best way of fitting a skylight is to rest the sides on the deck flush with the edge of the opening inside and edge-bolt them through carlings under the deck planks and then cover the joints between the carling, plank edge and skylight with a coaming on the inside.

Windows

Cut out the holes, following the shape on the plan, after the cabin topsides have been made but before they are fixed in place, so that you can work with the plank on the sawing bench. Plate glass is the best material for windows. Rectangular windows can be bought through yacht chandlers and marine stores. Dealers in surplus government stores sometimes have marine windows in stock at reasonable prices. When making windows in cabin trunks a rabbet should be cut, with the glass butting up against this, and

21 *Katie of Rhu*, 33 ft ketch-rigged motor-sailer based on a fishing boat hull, showing the type of design with enclosed wheelhouse, suitable for MFV or large lifeboat conversion

then on the outside of the glass hardwood quadrants should be fixed to hold the glass in position. The glass is bedded in a pliable compound such as Sealastic.

Doors

I have included a bridge deck in the plan, so either double doors or slides are possible. Doors are more trouble to make, slides more trouble to use. The doors should be designed to fold right back against the bulkhead. The slides should taper slightly downwards to prevent them sticking.

The hatch

The hatch in the foredeck is for headroom, ventilation, and as a means of escape; so make it large enough to get through (18 in. by 18 in. is the minimum inside measurement for a hatchway). It is a double-coaming rectangular hatch, resting on the deck, with one side hinged. There is no need to include a deadlight, but it would help to light the foc's'le. Fore-hatches tend to leak so they should be made and fitted with care. Maurice Griffiths' design for a double-coaming hatch is the only satisfactory leak-proof hatch that I know (Fig. 124).

This conversion is designed for coastal cruising. Her power unit must be strong enough to bring her home in any weather: I would think not less than 13 h.p. No engine is completely foolproof, so you will need auxiliary sail

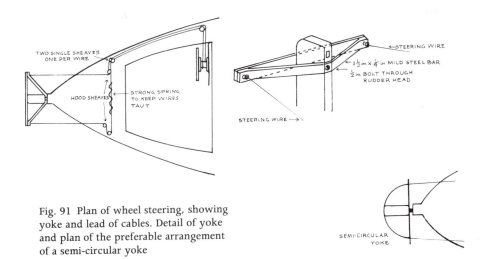

Fig. 91 Plan of wheel steering, showing yoke and lead of cables. Detail of yoke and plan of the preferable arrangement of a semi-circular yoke

for cruising; but put your mast in a tabernacle so that you can take the boat under bridges, on rivers and canals. Various rigs are possible. A single dipping lug is the simplest. The lugsail supplied to 26 ft and 28 ft lifeboats would do very well if slightly re-cut. Have a diagonal row of reef points sewn on the sail, so that in heavy weather the yard can run up and down the mast, with the tack of the sail made fast to a ring-bolt on the deck just aft of the mast. The yard is hooked by means of a single strop with an eye to the traveller which slides up and down the mast. The halyard leads from the traveller up to a sheave in the masthead and down to a cleat on the after end of the tabernacle box. Under this rig she should run or reach quite well. To dip the yard when going about you will need two tack-lines, one on each side of the mast, leading to a block on the deck and then aft. The yard can then be dipped from the cockpit by casting off her lee tack-line after setting up on the trip-line; then haul the trip-line aft to bring the yard round the mast. Set the tack up with the other tack-line. If the lugsail is considered too cumbersome, a small boomless gaff mainsail and a staysail will prove nearly as effective and in some ways easier to handle.

The mast should be a spruce spar 13 ft long, 4 in. diameter at the base tapering to $2\frac{1}{2}$ in. at the head, with a 4in. pole at the top, surmounted by a truck with a sheave for the signal halyards. Tabernacles can be made up by a blacksmith.

A wooden tabernacle case is not difficult to make. Step a 4 in. by 4 in. oak beam on the keelson and let it project about 1 ft through the cabin roof. Bolt substantial cheek pieces of 1 in. oak on either side, and let them project another foot upwards. The mast swivels inside the cheek pieces on a heavy $\frac{3}{4}$ in. galvanised bolt. To help the hull withstand the wringing strains when under sail, put in an extra 9 in. by 3 in. oak floor in the middle of the cabin. With the floor under the cabin bulkhead this should be enough.

Power cruiser conversions are often frightful monstrosities. If you carry the clench-planking up to the head of the new stempost, if you put the cabin topsides inboard of the gunwale and give them some tumblehome ($1\frac{1}{2}$ in. in 1 ft), make a fair curve in the ramp and coaming, place the skylight, hatches and other deck fittings judiciously, and choose an intelligent colour scheme, such as white topsides, a red ochre or putty coloured deck, and varnished cabin, you can make a handsome boat.

Engine position and stern tube installation
The engine will come just aft of the cabin bulkhead and the propeller shaft will pass through the sternpost. The bridge deck is a matter of personal

choice. If you have one it will house the engine. If not, you will have to build an engine casing.

Wheel steering
Handling the ship with a wheel is not instinctive to those accustomed to using a tiller, though it may be to bus drivers. To anyone who has learned to steer with a tiller, the only thing is to set to and learn to steer with a wheel. Provided the design of the gear and its layout follows good engineering practice, the feel of the wheel can be just as delicate as the feel of a tiller. Obviously, for any particular rudder fitted with both a tiller and cable steering, the cable and gear will add something to the frictional resistance of the rudder. But most rudders and tillers are set up on such inefficient bearings that the additional resistance of a good layout of cable, sprocket chain and pulleys (ball-bearing if possible) is so small that few people could detect any difference.

House the bearings for the pulleys beneath the deck, for the sake of dryness, and they will require practically no attention, provided they are well greased at the beginning of each season. The size of the drum or sprocket on the back of the wheel governs the mechanical advantage for any given length of rudder yoke. The best kind of rudder yoke is a quadrant radiating from a centre in line with the rudder hinge. This is most important, and should ensure that the cable is under constant tension with no hard spots or slack spots which will give resistance to motion and backlash. The pulleys must be firmly secured to the hull and at the correct alignment and the cable must not foul the pulley rim as it leads on or off. There must be no backlash at rest, but under way the cable at zero load can be a little slack but not slack enough to slip off the pulleys, even if guards are fitted to prevent this (and they are recommended).

This principle of steering is used in the control systems of aircraft. It is simple to construct and the pulleys and ball-bearings are obtainable at many stores dealing in aircraft surplus supplies.

Wheel steering is obviously most convenient for power cruisers. In this conversion the wheel is set on the port side of the bulkhead or bridge deck, and is connected to a yoke on the rudderhead by two wire cables. It is a good idea to have a short tiller, in case the wheel fails. There are many kinds of yokes; a quadrant is the best, but a simple and quite efficient one, made from $1\frac{1}{2}$ in. by $\frac{1}{4}$ in. mild steel bar, is shown in Fig. 91. The steering wires lead forward from the yoke to sheaves in the deck, just aft of the cockpit, then down to about cockpit bench level, where the starboard wire leads

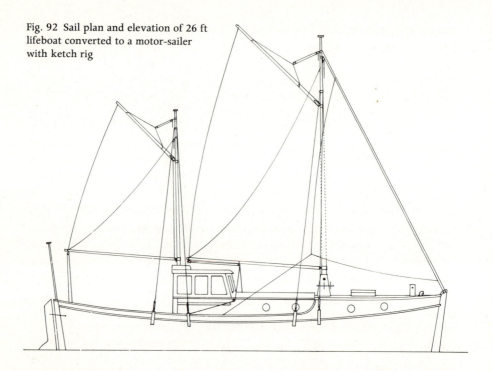

Fig. 92 Sail plan and elevation of 26 ft
lifeboat converted to a motor-sailer
with ketch rig

over to the port side. A strong spring is fitted at this point to keep the wires
taut. The wires then run along the inside of the boat to a double sheave level
with the 6 in. diameter drum forward of the wheel and on the same axle.
They lead up to the drum and five times round it. With the rudder amidships, and the wires taut, the middle wire on the drum has its lay opened and
a screw is then inserted and screwed into the drum. This prevents any slip
and anchors it firmly. An attractive wheel can be a feature of this craft, but
an old car steering wheel will serve just as well. Steering wheels can be
bought from yacht chandlers. Quarter-inch chain is in many ways better
than wire cable, but of course the drum has to be replaced by a sprocket.
The chains should be kept well greased.

Arrangement of the cockpit
This motor cruiser as originally designed had a large cockpit, 5 ft 6 in. long
from the after side of the bridge deck, which is 2 ft wide and affords further
seating space. The bridge deck is raised on the port side to take the wheel
mounting and to make a locker for the helmsman, or provide space for

mounting the binnacle. It has locker fronts that lift out, and will give plenty of space for stowage and make a perfectly good engine room. On the port side it might also provide space for part of one of the cabin bunks. The cockpit floor is 1 ft higher than the cabin floor, so there is plenty of room for the propeller shaft and engine bearers underneath.

Arrangement of foredeck, stowage of anchor, etc.
The foredeck has a large hatch 2 ft square directly in the centre, just forward of the cabin. The samson post comes 9 in. forward of the hatch. A 25 lb CQR or a 31 lb fisherman's anchor can be stowed lying fore and aft in chocks with, in the case of the fisherman, the stock outboard at the stemhead. The chain cable will lead down a hawsepipe to the chain locker in the stem. The samson post is a block of 4 in. by 4 in. hardwood, stepped on the deck and bolted through to chocks below. It is chamfered above deck to take the cable, and two galvanised or bronze bars are let through it for belaying lines. These bars should project at least 4 in. on either side.

Rigging, lead of sheets, etc.
The single halyard leads to a block on a strop and is belayed to a pin on the tabernacle. The mast is supported by a forestay, leading from the masthead to a rigging screw on the stemhead, and by two shrouds leading to rigging screws on the chainplates, which are 3 ft straps of gunmetal or galvanised iron fastened to the outside of the cabin sides and through-bolted to the inside of the original gunwale.

The lugsail and yard, when not in use, rest alongside the skylight on the port side. The fore end could be supported by a small chock on the foredeck, and the after end in a chock on the cabin roof. If gaff rigged, the procedure is as for the rigging of the 26 ft lifeboat ketch.

Ballast
You will need about 1000 lbs of ballast stowed amidships to prevent her from becoming cranky in a seaway and to obviate the danger of her capsizing under sail. This, with the weight of the motor, the chain and the rest of the gear, should be enough to make her sit firmly in the water.

Accommodation
You will of course suit your accommodation to your own needs. You can have anything from a very luxurious cabin for two to a spartan arrangement for sleeping four or five. I have compromised and planned three built-in

bunks, but there would be plenty of room for a fourth person to sleep on the cabin floor or on a camp bed.

The cabin is 10 ft long, 8 ft wide (at its widest) and with an average height of 5 ft 6 in. The foc's'le is 6 ft 6 in. wide at its widest, rapidly tapering to the stem. The average headroom is 5 ft 3 in. and the floor length is about 5 ft.

A 10 ft cabin is too short for two full-length bunks (6 ft 3 in.) so I have carried the port bunk 9 in. into the foc's'le and the after bunk projects right under the bridge deck. This arrangement, which leaves only about 15 in. clearance above the shins, may not be ideal, but I have assumed that the forward port bunk and the starboard bunk will be those normally in use. The bunks are 2 ft 6 in. wide at the head, which is quite generous. Dunlopillo mattresses are comfortable either for sleeping on or for sitting on during the day. As the bunks are rather wide for seats, I have put in a backrest which projects about 9 in. and also makes a useful shelf.

The companionway is on the starboard side and has two steps. As you enter the cabin the galley is just in front of you. It consists of a two-burner cooker mounted on a cupboard 2 ft high and separated from the starboard bunk by a bulkhead 3 ft 6 in. high. The bulkhead and the topsides are lined with Warite. Port of the companionway, on the after bulkhead, is a dresser cupboard, which reaches to the deck above and should be large enough to hold all the crockery and dry food.

Under each bunk there is a locker for stowing gear that does not suffer from the damp: tinned foods, bottles of beer, and boat's gear. Amidships there is a hinged table, with a compartment under the top for knives and forks, and a space below that for charts.

In the forward bulkhead of the cabin two narrow swing doors open into the foc's'le. There is a large open clothes cupboard at the foot of the port bunk and two shelves over the foot of the starboard bunk. The feet of both these bunks project into the foc's'le, but they are bulkheaded off by narrow tongue-and-groove planking. Entering the foc's'le you come under the fore-hatch. On the port side there is an open cupboard under the one that opens into the cabin. Further forward there is a shelf for stowing lamps and the like. The WC is in the bows, and beyond it is the chain locker right up in the stem. This can be boxed in, or not, as you think fit. I have left the starboard side clear, for stowing bags and so on. The cabin should be a very cheerful place with its large windows and opening skylight. The opening fore-hatch should also make the foc's'le well ventilated and well lit.

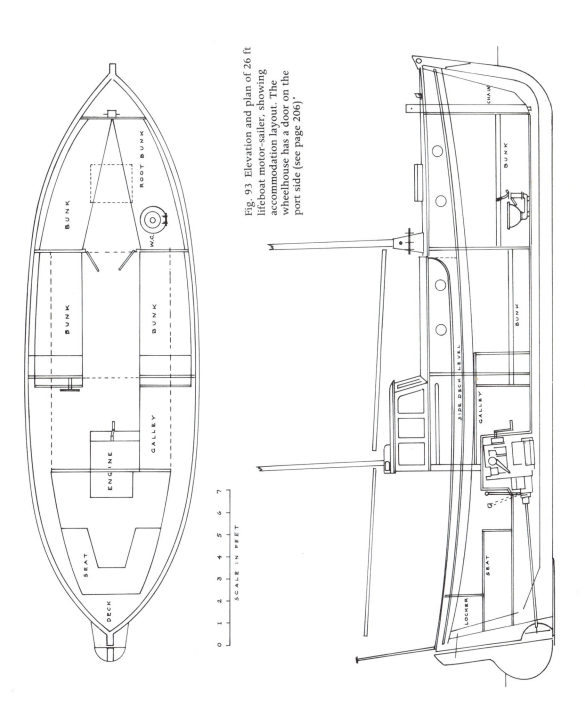

Fig. 93 Elevation and plan of 26 ft lifeboat motor-sailer, showing accommodation layout. The wheelhouse has a door on the port side (see page 206)

The canal cruiser

The chief stresses a canal cruiser might have to suffer are encountered when going through locks. Heavy rubbing strakes are essential, as are adequate cleats or bollards fitted fore and aft for the warps which one needs on a canal. Also it should be possible for the crew handling these warps to pass easily along the decks or over the cabin top. Apart from this, all one's design efforts can be towards comfortable accommodation, with full head-room at least amidships.

Fort Stevens: a 27 ft steel lifeboat conversion

This handsome little craft looks all of a piece and would make a very useful cruiser for inland waterways. The conversion of this 27 ft steel lifeboat into a motor-sailing cruiser was carried out by Mr Bill Jennings on the quayside at Woodbridge in Suffolk. What might appear to be a somewhat sophisticated design is really a model of simplicity. The fore and aft raised topsides are merely sheets of $\frac{1}{4}$ in. marine ply bolted to the outside of the gunwale. The bottom edges of these ply sheets neatly butt up against a moulded rubbing strake about 4 in. below the level of the gunwale, and plenty of Sealastic was forced in between the steel and the ply. Carlings were fitted along the top edges of these raised topsides and deck beams were checked into them. The decks were then planked with tongue-and-groove deal and finally canvased and painted.

The wheelhouse is a simple, woodframed, rectangular structure with

21 *Fort Stevens*, 27 ft lifeboat converted
to an inland waterways cruiser

Fig. 94 27 ft steel lifeboat converted
into a canal cruiser

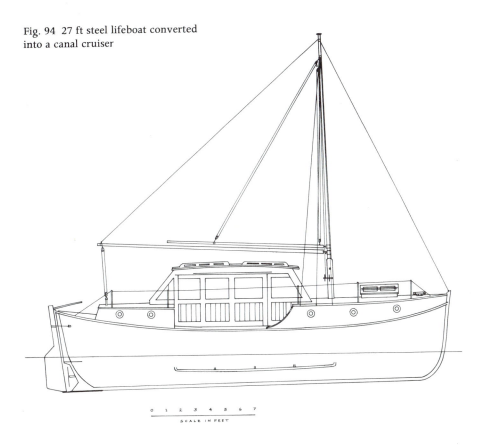

SCALE IN FEET

sliding doors on both sides. For these the normal domestic sliding door
technique was used with a track at top and bottom. In contrast to the white
topsides of the little ship, the coach roof has varnished sides. Side decks
about 1 ft wide run along either side of the wheelhouse, so facilitating
passage fore and aft. This is an important factor in canal work where the
crew may have to hurry to pick up or cast off a warp. The sloping ends of
this wheelhouse and the fact that it is set well inboard add greatly to the
appearance of the conversion.

Accommodation
There is full headroom under the wheelhouse roof and sitting headroom in
the fore and aft cabins. There are two bunks in the aft cabin and two in the
forward. In the wheelhouse there is a dinette to port and a bunk to star-

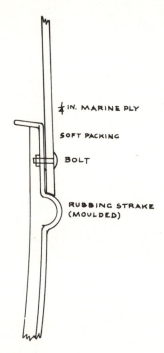

Fig. 95 Detail showing how new plywood topsides are fastened to the steel topsides of the lifeboat

¼ IN. MARINE PLY

SOFT PACKING

BOLT

RUBBING STRAKE (MOULDED)

board. The WC is right up forward. The steering gear is to port and the engine is situated at the after end of the wheelhouse, with a table top over it. *Fort Stevens* is driven by a six-cylinder Austin engine—a powerful unit that runs quietly and uses a lot of petrol! She has over 1500 lbs of concrete ballast cast in the bilges of the boat. This provides additional strength as well as weight.

Stern gear installation

The lifeboat's sternpost was rounded at the foot, so a wide $\frac{3}{8}$ in. steel plate was welded to it, to allow for the full aperture for the propeller. Another piece of $\frac{3}{8}$ in. plate was welded to the end of the keel to make the bottom of the propeller gap. Under that, and continuing forward along the keel for about 12 in., a 2 in. by $\frac{1}{2}$ in. steel bar was welded onto this to make a gudgeon. The propeller shaft came out of the stern of the boat, close alongside the keel. It projected about 3 in. into the propeller aperture. The shaft log was of cement inside a transverse wooden shuttering.

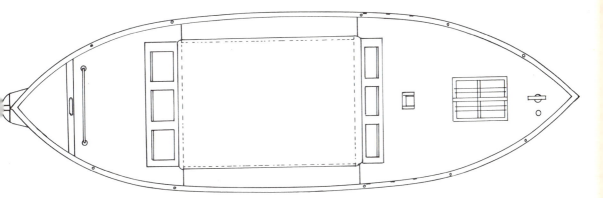

Fig. 96 Deck plan of 27 ft canal cruiser

Steering gear and gear lever
Two triangular-shaped pieces of tread plate about 12 in. long were welded onto either side of the rudder stock about 1 ft from its top and wires were taken through slots cut in the topsides. These were run over pulleys and then along the port side to the steering wheel. The gear lever on the engine was operated by means of a lever coupled to a long steel bar that ran aft to the engine under the wheelhouse floor.

Rig
This cruiser carries quite a useful spread of sail, with a gaff mainsail and a foresail. The mast is set in a tabernacle. For canal use these sails might be dispensed with, but for use on rivers, lakes, etc. they would add greatly to the enjoyment of the crew. Because the boat has no false keel, for windward work she would have to rely on her engine.

Rubbing strakes
Fort Stevens was not fitted with rubbing strakes, but for canal use these are essential. One could be fitted about 4 in. below the existing moulded steel rail. This should be made of larch and be fairly substantial and not less than $1\frac{1}{2}$ in. thick. A further strake of the same dimension could be fixed amidships for about 12 ft fore and aft and about a foot below the other one. These would both be through-bolted to the steel plate of the topsides. The

upper strakes may need steaming to take up the curves fore and aft. These strakes should be regarded as being expendable. They are there to do what their name says.

26 ft lifeboat converted into a motor-sailer

The construction of this conversion follows the same line as the one on page 188 for the foredeck, with a raised stempost. An additional strake will be added to the full length of the boat, and a final strake, which will be considerably deeper, will come down in a sharp curve just aft of the mast and will then run the full length of the boat, acting as a gunwale. I suggest that this be made of iroko or mahogany. The cabin trunk and the wheelhouse will not be to the full width of the ship, because there will be side decks of at least 12 in. in width. These side decks will be fitted at the top of the additional strake, supported by half-beams checked into the carlings.

The cabin trunk and wheelhouse, which looks quite complicated, is really a fairly simple box-like structure with parallel vertical sides. There will be full standing headroom in the wheelhouse both for steering the ship and working at the galley and there is a sliding door into the cockpit. The engine is fully accessible, for its box can have removable top and sides. The roof of the wheelhouse has only a slight camber. There is a bulkhead at the forward end of the wheelhouse with an open doorway in the centre. There are bunks on either side of the cabin: in each case the sleeper's feet will be under sideboards projecting through the bulkhead into the wheelhouse; there is 5 ft of headroom in the cabin. Double swing doors lead into the foc's'le, where there is a fixed berth to port, a WC and lockers to starboard, with a Root berth to swing down over these.

This conversion is rather more sophisticated than the previous one. If she is to be a proper motor-sailer she should have at least an additional 6 in. deep false keel, through-bolted to heavy floors. For the construction of this follow the plans for the 26 ft lifeboat ketch or the 27 ft lifeboat cutter conversions. Also, her ballast ought to be increased to at least 1500 lbs.

26 ft lifeboat converted to a motor fishing vessel

Numerous fishing lifeboat conversions are in use along the coasts of Britain and northern Europe. In its simplest form, this conversion need only have an engine installed, with adequate bearers and floors in the way of the engine. If the lifeboat was originally powered with an engine she is almost ready for use, and will certainly have less sheer than a boat designed for rowing, so is a better proposition for conversion.

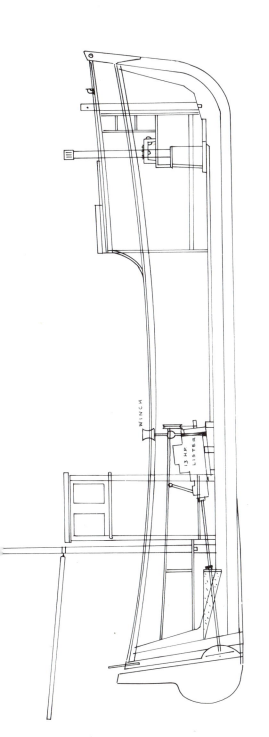

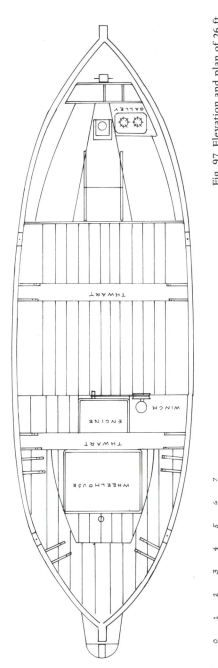

Fig. 97 Elevation and plan of 26 ft lifeboat converted into a fishing boat, showing accommodation and layout

The conversion of a lifeboat into a fishing vessel may amount to no more than decking in the fore part to provide shelter. If a proper little cabin is wanted, then the stempost should be increased in height by about a foot and the topsides built up to this height, either by lapstrake planks or false timbers, or with a single wide plank or sheet of marine plywood set inside the gunwale, which could act as a carling.

For estuary and inshore trawling a wheelhouse is an enormous comfort. This can be placed astern or up forward. In either case one should leave as much of the boat clear as is possible for handling nets or trawls. If you do plan to do any trawling a capstan is essential. This has to be securely mounted against a thwart. It can be made up from a rear axle of a motor car.

A wheelhouse in the forward position can be seated on the foredeck and firmly bolted to carlines. If at the after end of the boat it may well be standing up like a sentry box, so it needs bolting down very securely to heavy floors and fore-and aft members. Even so, I think it would be well for it to have some lateral support at least to the height of the thwarts. A re-positioned thwart placed just in front of it, or the side benches at the stern of the boat could serve this purpose. For further details about wheelhouse construction, see page 266.

The foc's'le cabin can have bunks on either side. There would be room for simple cooking arrangements and a coal stove is absolutely essential for any winter fishing. There is no possible room for a WC so a bucket would have to serve for this purpose. In spite of the reliability of diesel engines, I think a simple two-masted rig is worth considering, with a small mizzen astern of the wheelhouse, if the wheelhouse is at the back of the boat, and a main mast abutting the bulkhead of the foc's'le. This could have a loose-footed gaff sail and a single headsail. With this rig the boat will run and reach. The hull will need a certain amount of stiffening and not less than 1000 lbs of ballast under the floorboards. The design, as I have drawn it, has only a mizzen, which serves the dual purpose of steadying the boat and keeping her head to windward.

Trawl capstan

The old Austin 7 rear axle is particularly suitable for the mechanical parts of a capstan, for it is fairly small and quite robust. One of the halfshafts is removed, the axle tube is cut just inside the brake drum and a cap is welded to what will be the bottom of the tube. The differential is locked by welding, and by making use of only the crown wheel and pinion is converted into a simple angle drive. At the outer and now top end of the other half of the

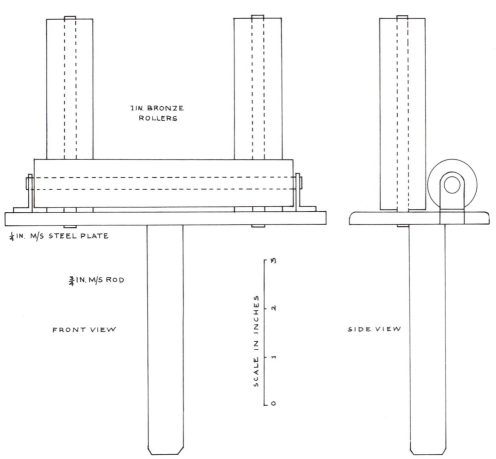

1IN. BRONZE ROLLERS

¼ IN. M/S STEEL PLATE

¾ IN. M/S ROD

FRONT VIEW

SCALE IN INCHES

SIDE VIEW

Fig. 98 Fishing boat fairlead (mongoggle) fixed in the same manner as a rowlock, with the steel rod below the plate fitting into the existing rowlock plates in the gunwale cappings

axle, remove the brake drum, leaving the hub plate in position. To this plate bolt the capstan head, which can be made of wood reinforced with brass strip, or cast in iron or alloy.*

A V-pulley (12 in. diameter) is fitted to the end of the pinion and a $4\frac{1}{2}$ in. Fennerlock pulley is fitted to the end of the crankshaft, or in the case of a Lister diesel, to the starting handle shaft, which is $1\frac{1}{2}$ in. in diameter. The

*These capstan heads can be supplied by Frank Knights (Shipwrights) Ltd, Ferry Quay, Woodbridge. These trawl windlasses have been designed by Keith Cutmore, who is the engineering director of this firm.

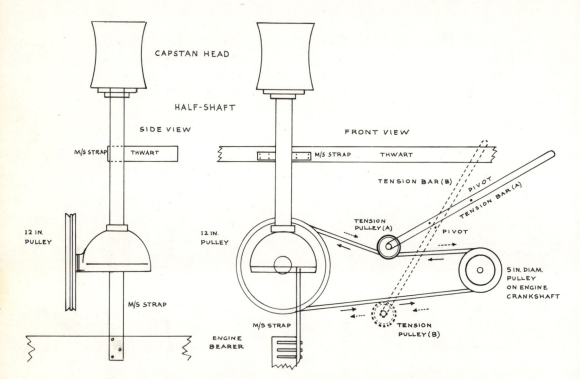

Fig. 99 Fishing boat capstan made up of a half-shaft of the rear axle of an Austin 7, front and side view. Note: the tension bar has been shown (A, B) in two positions. The tension pulley has to come on the side of the belt which has not got the drive on it. The drive, of course, has to come on the pulling side of the belt

V-belts are also made by Fennerlock and are put on with a slack fit, running over a pivoted idler pulley. A control lever connected to this idler pulley will draw the pulley up, so tightening the V-belt and starting the drive on the capstan. The position of the capstan is dictated by the need for the 12 in. V-pulley on the pinion to be in line with the driving pulley on the engine. With the capstan head set vertically, the trawl lines should run horizontally from the capstan to the gunwales. Here they will pass over and between pulley assemblies called mongoggles. These pulley assemblies are made up of two 2 in. brass tubes revolving vertically on spindles and another one revolving horizontally. These are bolted to a brass plate which has a 5 in. vertical bar underneath inserted into a rowlock plate on the gunwale. The capstan must be very firmly braced, perhaps with an A-bracket to a thwart and its base set in a socket on the engine bearers. The arms of the A-bracket can be further strengthened with steel webs welded to them. With the wheelhouse aft and a raised foredeck forward, the trawl lines will run from the quarter and just aft of the forepeak bulkhead. Once one is trawling, the boat is steered on the trawl, so an additional line taken from the opposite quarter is made fast about 20 ft out on the after trawl line. A hard pull on this line will bring the boat's head round. If the wheelhouse is set up forward, this will leave the whole of the after part of the ship clear so additional pulleys can be set over the sternpost. With a stern pulley the capstan head can be set horizontally, but this means that only the stern pulley can be used for the trawl line.

A refinement for a vertical capstan head is to have an additional mongoggle* set up 12 in. or so from it, with a gate on the top, so that the trawl line cannot jump out of it when the boat is pitching in a seaway. This will still keep the line horizontal as it comes to the capstan head.

* There is some confusion about the spelling of this word, another version is molgogger

NINE

Larger craft suitable for conversion

Colchester oyster smacks, Thames bawleys, Cornish luggers and pilchard drivers, Morecambe Bay prawners and Lancashire nobbies are all types of traditional fishing boat that can be found around the coasts of England. Though deriving from boats originally designed for sail, many of these old fishing boats will have been built with engines in them and some of them, apart from the use of a steadying sail, may never have sailed. The Cornish lugger, for instance had auxiliary engines as early as 1910. Within ten years of that date these luggers were fully powered with two engines. Their rigs were modified and their sails were finally relegated to steadying the boats or keeping their heads to the wind. Most of these fishing boats can still be converted back to sail and made to sail well either under their

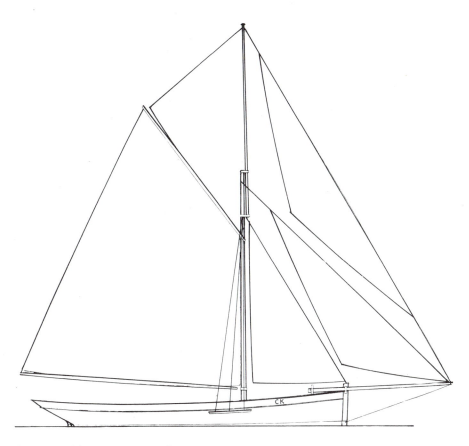

Fig. 100 Colchester oyster smack
(Science Museum)

traditional rigs or, perhaps less well, with more modern sail plans. This
change of sail plan needs some caution, for the modern high aspect ratio
bermudan sail plan lacks the drive and the sail area necessary to push most
of these deep displacement hulls through the water.

   One of the more satisfying aspects of converting a fishing boat to a cruiser
is to attempt some act of restoration, so that she approaches as nearly as
possible the boat as originally designed. Deckhouses, cabin trunks, etc.
should be designed to interfere as little as possible with the boat's original
appearance. If you want a floating caravan this kind of conversion is not
for you. Fishing boat hulls suitable for conversion are not limited to the
English coasts. There are various splendid Scottish types such as fifies,

zulus and Loch Fyne skiffs. There is of course need for caution in buying these old boats. A careful survey must be carried out (see page 219). Various types of motor sailing yachts, based on the lines of these Scottish boats, have been built in recent years. I made one cruise on the West Coast of Scotland in a boat of this kind. She was an extremely able craft, driven by a hefty great diesel. Her sails were a secondary feature, in fact they were hardly more than an ornament. In converting the design of these fishing boats to yachts, the beam of their fishing boat sisters had been drastically reduced, as presumably the builders considered their gloriously wide decks so much waste of space (and timber) for a cabin cruiser.

The coasts of Europe can show an infinite variety of fishing boats that could provide a good basis for conversion. There are various double-ended Scandinavian boats that convert well. There are types of tunny boat in Brittany that could be made into splendid yachts. In Portugal, at Sesimbra and Nazaré, they build fishing boats that would provide a most interesting basis for conversion. In both Scandinavia and Portugal it might well be worth considering buying new hulls (which are not expensive), with engines installed so that they could be brought back to this country under

23 The ultimate in restoration: *Boadicea*, originally built at Maldon, Essex in 1808, after her complete re-build at Tollesbury

24 Port side – note heavy channels (see page 226)

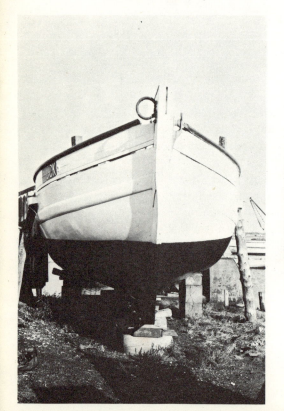

25 Foredeck, teak deckhouse and hatch caulked and payed but not cleaned off

26 Windlass on *Boadicea*

Fig. 101 Loch Fyne skiff (Science Museum)

Fig. 102 Shetland sixern, after drawings by Arthur Johnston

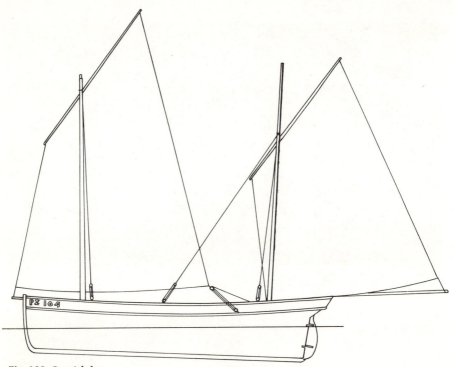

Fig. 103 Cornish lugger

their own power for completion. In some countries (not Great Britain), if they come in on their own bottoms, I believe that they are subject to less import duty.

In Holland you can still buy old botters, boeiers, tjalks, hengsts and hoogaars in both wood and steel. These old boats, superbly suited to shoal waters and estuary fishing, are not ideal for passage making and deep water sailing. Having said that, they provide a great deal of room, much character and a closer link with the past ages of sail than anything else afloat today. The wooden hulled boats are massively built of oak, but as when buying any old craft, they do need a careful survey. Because of the size of the timbers and the thickness of the planking, extensive replacements of wood-work can be expensive in material cost alone. If they are wood built and stripped down to the bare wood and then oiled or varnished, they look wonderful, just like a beautiful piece of old furniture. And they can cost a fortune to maintain, either in time or labour costs.

The conversion of these Dutch boats can be complicated or very simple. A few years ago, I went aboard a botter at Enkhuizen on the Zuider Zee.

She had had the minimum amount of conversion work done to her, but all the tar had been scraped off her timbers and planking. This had taken one old man, working in his spare time, the best part of two years. The fore part, as in all botters, was decked over with a steeply sloping deck leading up to the bow. Under this deck there was a huge cabin with a floor space of about 12 ft by 10 ft. There was only 4 ft 3 in. headroom aft, but about 5 ft 6 in. forward. It was lit by deadlights let into the deck and there was a hanging brass lamp. Up in the bows a bulkhead had been built to shut off the chain locker and against this there were two bunks, one above the other. There was an old circular iron stove with its iron chimney poking through the deck. There was a camp bed, a couple of stools, a case of beer and nothing else. I have written elsewhere about this old botter.* I still have vivid memories of her romantic old cabin with its smell of Stockholm tar and the mellow warmth of its oiled planks and timbers. As we drank beer with our Dutch friends in this splendid if spartan cabin, I felt we might well have been sitting the forepeak of the *Hispaniola*, listening to Long John Silver, spinning yarns of the Spanish Main. This was back in 1958, and she was eighty years old then.

Amongst other large craft suitable for conversion, lifeboats (as opposed to ships' lifeboats) are still a good proposition. Scandinavian lifeboats (and pilot boats) of the Colin Archer type make wonderful sailing cruisers. RNLI boats will sail but are probably better as motor-sailers. These craft are double-diagonal planked and are well built. The old pulling types have a very low freeboard and need their topsides building up. They are difficult boats to convert effectively. When converted they tend to look slabsided.

Large craft

A number of Motor Fishing Vessels have been built for the British Admiralty. These range from 50 ft to 72 ft overall. The so-called 45 ft Admiralty type MFV is actually 50 ft overall. These smaller MFVs have a beam of 15 ft and displace about 25 tons. They are usually larch planked on heavy oak timbers. They are very solid and strongly built boats, only intended for motor propulsion. They can roll like anything, so steadying sails are worth while. They are of course very roomy craft; in fact one could live aboard one.

In 1958 we were in Lowestoft harbour about to set out for my first North Sea crossing. A straight-stemmed, gaff rigged cutter anchored alongside us. She was a characterful little craft with a 9 ft bowsprit poking through her bulwarks on the starboard side of her stemhead. This was Dr E. A. Pye's

* *A Taste for Sailing,* John Lewis. Adlard Coles Ltd, London, 1969

Fig. 104 Morecambe Bay prawner
(Science Museum)

Moonraker of Fowey. Originally she was the *Lily*, a lugger built in Looe in the 1890s. Dr Pye bought her at Polperro in the 1930s for £25. This was before she was converted. At the ripe age of 53 this converted fishing boat was sailed by the Pyes to the West Indies and Florida and back to England. And a year or so later they sailed her all the way to northern British Columbia and back home again. She was 29 ft long and had a beam of 10 ft. She drew 6 ft aft when fully loaded with her gear and was, as the saying is, all boat. 'Everything was to be as simple as possible: lanyards, not rigging screws; paraffin lamps, not electricity; a Primus in gimbals for cooking . . .'. These few sentences of Dr Pye's should be pinned up on the main beam of every conversion. You cannot make silk purses out of sow's ears, nor glamourous yachts out of aged fishing boats. The beauty of a good conversion lies not in apeing the antics of expensive yachts, but in that kind of deep-seated beauty which is one of the results of perfect fitness for purpose. *Moonraker of Fowey* was such a conversion. May yours be another.

Surveying

It is obviously common sense to have any boat surveyed before you buy her. If you know a professional surveyor he can save you a lot of time and money by going over the craft for you. If, on the other hand, you employ a surveyor that you don't know, he will nearly always warn you off. He has to protect himself and all old boats suffer from the defects due to age. Having said all that, it might be as well if you did the job yourself. The following notes are a rough guide.

If it smells bad, it probably is bad. Dry rot has a particularly pungent smell.

If it is freshly painted, view it with suspicion.

If the bottom is cemented and it is *not* a fishing smack, view with suspicion. Fishing smacks were nearly all cemented as soon as they were built and there is rarely any trouble under the cement. Such trouble as there is will be along the planks where they abut the top of the cement.

If the inside is lined throughout, view with suspicion.

Places where you are likely to find rot are at the timberheads, at the ends of the deck beams and in the covering board. One or two rotten beams may not be too bad, but a rotten shelf to which the beams are fastened is a fearful job to replace.

Look at the chainplates and their fastenings, to see if they are badly rusted.

If the rudder is outboard, i.e. hung from a transom, or from the sternpost as in lifeboats, there should be no trouble here, but if supported in a trunk through a counter, examine carefully.

Lift floorboards and move ballast. With a marline spike prick the floors, keelson (if the boat has one), top of the keel, mast step and deadwoods at stem and stern. Look out for heavy shakes in oak knees at stem and stern. These may need tieing with iron straps. Replacing floors is not too difficult; replacing cut frames is rather more of a job.

If the deck is made of ply, look out for delamination, particularly at the stem, stern and along the edges.

If the deck or cabin top is canvased, look at it with suspicion, particularly

Fig 105 Harwich bawley (Science Museum)

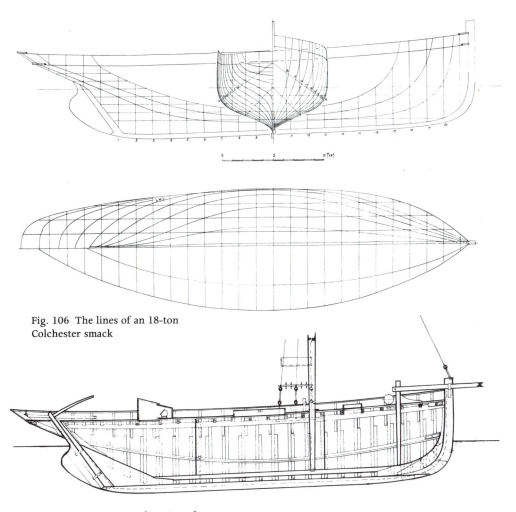

Fig. 106 The lines of an 18-ton
Colchester smack

Fig. 107 Construction elevation of
Colchester smack

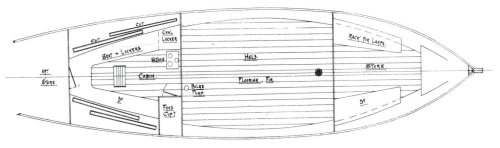

Fig. 108 Deck and accommodation
layout of Colchester smack

if it is loose or bubbling up. Have it raised to see if there is any rot below.

Spars: longitudinal shakes are not important, providing the wood has not rotted inside the cracks. Apart from using a marline spike to prick for soft or rotten wood, a hammer is useful. A soft tap on good wood gives a sharp note, on rotten wood a more muffled note. If iron fastened, examine for rot round the fastenings, particularly in mahogany. Also examine for rusty or loose nails. Complete refastening is a big job. If copper fastened, see that the rooves are hard up against the timbers. If they are not it may merely mean that the timber has shrunk. If this is the case, they can be hardened up.

Hood ends: examine these to see that the screws are firm. If these screws are of brass, they may well have perished. Refastening is not difficult.

Planking: apart from obvious scores and scrapes, which can be easily filled, examine along the waterline to see if there is any rot. Also examine the garboards for the same purpose.

Keel bolts: draw out one or two of these to see what condition they are in. The fact that they may look perfectly all right at the head does not mean that they may not have wasted away to nothing in the middle.

If the boat has an engine, there is rarely any rot or trouble in the keel or floors below the machine, presumably because of the preserving effect of dripping sump oil.

Engine: you will either know enough about machinery to know that it is all right, or you will not. In the latter case get a mechanic to go over it for you. Apart from electrics, water pumps are the most obvious weakness in marine engines.

Rot: *Merulius lacrymans*, the so-called dry rot, grows in places that are damp and have little ventilation. It can be recognised by a grey bloom over the surface of the wood. The wood has the appearance of being charred, that is the surface is broken up into a rectangular pattern or transverse and longitudinal shakes. The spores of this beastly thing can reach every part of the boat and its greyish strands can spread over paint and metal in search of bare wood. Without moisture, the fungus cannot live. It also cannot live below water, for it needs oxygen. If your prospective boat is only slightly affected with dry rot, it can be dealt with, but if I saw it any-where in a boat, I would view the rest of the craft with great suspicion. The treatment is as follows: all affected wood must be removed. Paint every bit of the rest of the boat with a mixture of sodium flouride mixed with water, in the proportion of a pound to a two-gallon bucket of water. It is very poisonous. In addition, and for good measure, fumigate the boat by mixing 9 oz. of potassium permanganate with one pint of formalin in a bucket and leave in the boat for several days with all the openings blocked up. Then open up and air for several days. Any new wood that is going into the boat should be treated with Cuprinol or hot creosote. Rot nearly always comes from damp or rainwater, not from seawater.

Wood borers, particularly gribble, can cause a lot of damage to places like rudder trunks. *Teredo navalis* is also found in some European waters; like the gribble they bore along the grain and can be detected, as can the gribble, by hammering and pricking. The bottom of a boat that is badly infested with these borers should not be considered. Woodlice may often be found in old smacks. They eat sodden wood. Tar varnish is a better deterrent against borers than antifouling. They flourish in salt water; a boat moved to fresh water will become de-infested of borers, as will one left on shore for some months.

Fishing boats, their restoration and conversion

The difference between converting a 26 ft ship's lifeboat into a canal cruiser or even a seagoing sailing boat and converting or restoring a heavy-timbered fishing boat such as a Colchester smack or a Cornish lugger is so great that it really sorts out the men from the boys. To begin with, a ship's lifeboat will be of no great age and so apart from minor damage such as broken cappings or at the most a cracked plank, may not need any restoration work on her, whereas a smack of seventy or more years may need a lot of work. Her frames may be riddled with wood borers, her planks along the waterline may be rotten, her hood ends badly frayed. Her covering boards and timberheads will almost certainly need attention. She may even need a new stem or sternpost. If she needs new floors the keelson will have to be lifted, and the concrete that fills the bottom of most of these boats will have to be chipped out. Surprisingly, most of these old boats are in good shape below the concrete, but rot has often set in where the top of the concrete abuts the planks, where water may have lodged. If the smack needs a new mast, you will need to find a tree at least the size of a telegraph pole. If she needs a new keel, you are faced with the ultimate problem of whether to rebuild entirely.

This may sound rather intimidating, but several people I know who have either converted or restored old fishing boats knew absolutely nothing about shipbuilding. These old boats were simply built, by relatively simple folk. There is always a large margin of safety in the size of their timbers and the thickness of their planks. Working on them is not like

27 *Bona*, Leigh bawley, built at
Brightlingsea in 1902, after her
restoration

trying to rebuild a Camper & Nicholson J-Class yacht or a Clyde-built 8-metre, which were made like beautiful pieces of furniture.

Theory has been put into practice on the rivers Blackwater and Colne in Essex. Here a number of fishing smacks and bawleys are sailing, looking very much as they must have done when they were just built. *Iris,* restored by Charles Harker of Abberton, for instance, is a 'middle-sized' smack, built with shallow draft for dredging the oyster beds off Bradwell. These shallow-hulled smacks do not make very good conversions, but they come into their own if, as an act of faith, they are restored to their proper purpose. About three-quarters of *Iris*'s working life was probably never outside the Blackwater. She spent her time just trawling or dredging between Mersey Quarters and the Bench Head. Maybe in fair weather, if the fish were there, she would go through the Ray Sand Channel and as far as Burnham. Such shallow draft smacks if used as yachts are not good sea boats, because of their low freeboard and great weight. In a seaway they can be very wet, possibly even dangerous. Yet in the waters for which they were built, rigged as they were intended, used for pottering about in shoal waters or used for fishing, and handled as the fishermen handled them, they are an absolute delight.

It is a very splendid thing that they are being kept sailing by these enthusiasts, for not only are they prolonging the lives of these old boats but they are helping to perpetuate the skills that might so easily be lost. These restorers and converters learnt their job as they went along. Such information as I can give you here can only present some of the problems involved in this kind of work.

When undertaking the conversion of a fishing boat, the first job one has to do is to clean her out. This may sound pretty obvious, but it is a bigger job than it sounds. In order to clean out the inside of the boat, all linings will have to be removed, and they will probably be smashed in the process. Behind the linings, if they have been there since the boat was built, there will almost certainly be a filthy mess, made up of old sawdust, shavings and mud. It may well be alive with woodlice, if with nothing worse.

After clearing away this muck, the boat should be hosed out with clean water and scrubbed with caustic soda. Then a blowlamp should be run over the whole of the inside surface to dry it out properly.

The next thing is to take stock and decide what needs renewing. No doubt some decisions about this will have been taken at the time of the survey, but by the time the inside has been stripped and cleaned, more things may have come to light. The most likely replacements are the covering boards and bulwark timbers. The sheer strakes and the planks along the waterline and where the concrete ballast abuts them may need replacing, as may some of the frames. The stempost is often pretty shaky, and so is the apron behind it. In smacks with a counter, the sternpost is often rotten in the way of the rudder trunk. All these replacements are fairly straightforward. To put in new shelves to support the deck beams is a fearful job; to put in a new keel is maybe even worse! Once one has got to the stage of having to do these very major jobs, it almost amounts to an entire rebuild. This is what Michael Frost had to do with his beautiful little Maldon smack *Boadicea*. To rebuild a boat bit by bit is a much more difficult job than building a new boat.

If any major replacements have to be done it is most important that great pains should be taken to prevent the hull from going out of shape. In the case of *Boadicea,* before her keel was removed she was reframed inside, and heavy temporary bilge keels were fitted to take the weight while the old keel was being taken out of her. If the concrete ballast has to be taken out, there is nothing for it but to work away with a cold chisel. In the case of a rebuild, one can be fairly drastic, but if it is only a matter of replacing a few floors, then care has to be taken not to damage the structure of the boat.

Mayflower is not a conversion but a restoration. She was built by Aldus in 1887. Her restorer and owner is Donald Rainbird of West Mersea. *Mayflower* was bought as a wreck after a butane gas and petrol vapour explosion. The boat was dredging below the Bench Head on the Blackwater, when a violent explosion blew the bows apart and lifted the deck and deck beams, blew part of the stern away, and blew one member of the crew out of the cabin and the other overboard. In spite of the boat making a lot of water, they beached her at West Mersea.

It was in this sorry state that Donald Rainbird bought *Mayflower* for £35. He set to work to repair the damage. The explosion had mainly damaged rotten timbers that needed replacing, so it was not such a disastrous happening. Donald Rainbird spent over £100 on timber alone. The first job was to put in a new apron, shaped from templates, and three new forward frames on each side. The next was to fit new beam shelves on each side and then to redeck her with $1\frac{1}{2}$ in. fir. The next was to make a new mast. He bought a heavy larch pole, shaped it octagonally and then rounded it from above the decks to the hounds, finally tapering it off to the truck. Within a couple of years the pole had developed diagonal shakes and the cheek pieces of the hounds were out of the horizontal midships line by 45°. Apart

28 Brightlingsea fishing smack *Mayflower*, built in 1887, after restoration to a working smack. The stanchions and lifelines are removable when trawling

29 *Iris*, fishing smack built at Brightlingsea in 1903, after restoration in her winter quarters in Peldon Creek
30 Leigh bawley *Bona*, showing her wide uncluttered decks

31 *Shamrock*, fishing smack built at
Brightlingsea in 1900, converted to a
cruising boat

from looking a little odd if one peered up the mast, it was of no consequence and such shakes did not appear to weaken the pole. They were filled with soft filler (Sealastic).

The living accommodation in *Mayflower* is simple. In the forepeak she has three berths and a galley. The cabin aft is used mainly for storage, or as an engine room if one is ever installed. 'It would have to be a quarter in-stallation,' Donald Rainbird said, 'for the old stern tube is not only covered by new stern timbers, but one of the new bolts has been drilled right through it.'

One of the reasons for including descriptions of *Iris, Mayflower* and *Boadicea* (restorations rather than conversions) is to show what can be done with very old or badly damaged boats. They are now all most covetable craft.

Shamrock – a conversion of a 44 ft Colchester smack

Shamrock was built at Brightlingsea in 1900. She is one of the largest of the Colchester smacks, 44 ft overall and 37 ft on the waterline. She had been through various hands and a few winters ago, during a hard frost, she was sunk at her moorings, either because ice floes had cut through her planking or, more probably, because her caulking had been forced out of her top-sides. Whatever the reason, when the ice thawed, down she went. Who-ever raised her succeeded in pulling out her stempost. She was sold as a wreck to a local boatbuilder for £50. He patched her up, scarphed in a new stempost and sold her to a man who built a large wheelhouse over the engine and ran her as a motor boat. Her engine was a 16 h.p. water cooled Lister diesel.

Bryan Thomas, a young Colchester architect, bought her for cruising with his wife and four very young sons and various other friends and relations. The first thing he did after drawing out plans for the conversion was to demolish the wheelhouse; the next, to remove the engine for a thorough overhaul. The engine is still ashore, for the owner said, 'I thought it a good idea to have a season under sail alone.' This was a brave decision for someone who had never sailed a smack before, but it was a very sen-sible one. The very day she entered the water after her refit she won the smack race from Brightlingsea to Heybridge.

Structural work so far has consisted of replacing seven frames on each side and three planks at the turn of the bilge on the starboard side. Both planks and frames were very spongy, particularly where they abutted the concrete in the ship's bottom. (All these smacks were concreted.) These planks had also suffered from wood borers. The deck was all right, but most of the covering board and practically all the stanchions and bulwark planks had to be replaced. *Shamrock*'s timbers were in pairs, so Bryan Thomas replaced the more badly damaged of each pair. These new frames were laminated ¾ in. marine ply to make up a thickness of 4 in. They were side bolted to the remaining member of the pair as well as having the planks nailed to them. Her mast, gaff, boom and bowsprit were all in quite good shape. At the moment she is sailing without a topmast, though her owner intends her to have one. The standing rigging was all right but she needed a complete new set of running rigging.

The conversion

This is about the most discreet conversion (as opposed to a restoration) of a smack that I have ever seen. Almost the only obvious departures from the customary hatches in a smack of this class were the cabin trunk amidships and the trunk and hatchway over the engine room aft. The main cabin trunk was only 9 ft 6 in. long by 4 ft 6 in. wide. It was fitted athwartships with a sliding hatch, the slide being of Perspex. Its height had been kept

32 *Shamrock*, port side, showing position of helmsman on these smacks; only the bawleys have steering wells. Bulwarks aft still have to be planked

down so that it barely showed above the bulwarks, yet it gave full standing headroom in the cabin. Below decks (at the time of writing) nothing is complete, apart from necessary structural work. Some of the most time-taking work was the breaking out of the concrete ballast in order to replace the damaged floors. Below the concrete everything was in quite good condition.

To get *Shamrock* to the condition she is now in has taken three years, and Bryan Thomas showed some wisdom in getting in a season's sailing before completing the fitting out below. All converters and restorers might bear this in mind or they may never get a sail in their massive old boats. The fun to be had by young children in a big boat like this is unlimited. They can roar round the wide open side decks or chase about below decks with no harm to anyone or anything, except perhaps to their parents' nerves. For open sea work, stanchions (possibly removable), safety nets and lifelines

Fig. 109 Sail plan of *Shamrock*, 44 ft overall Colchester smack conversion by Bryan Thomas

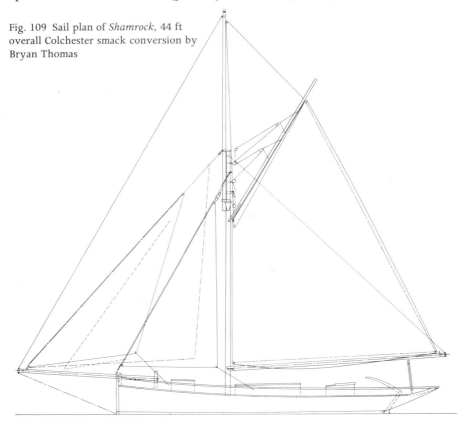

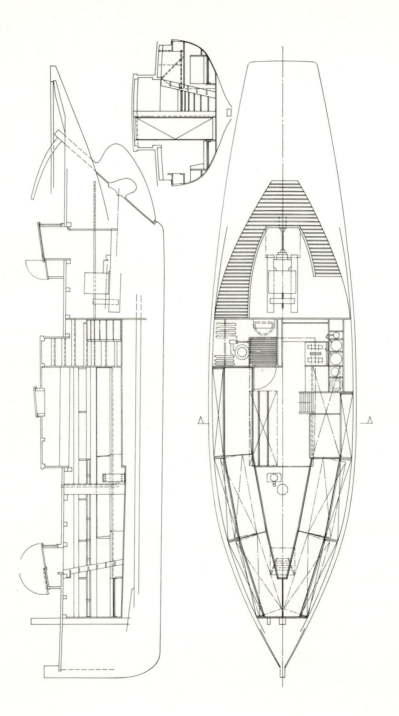

Fig. 110 Elevation, section and plan of *Shamrock*, showing conversion layout

would be advisable, if you want to return to port with as many small fry as you started out with.

I sailed in *Shamrock* on a warm day in October. The old ship did everything she was asked to do. We only had light winds but she slipped through the water in an impressive manner. *Shamrock* with her unusual size is a very fast ship and very clean through the water, leaving little or no turbulance behind her.

Shamrock's colour scheme, though not much of a departure from the traditional, was attractive. Her sails, of course, were tanned a deep brick red. Her deck was stone coloured, her deckhouses, which were built of deal, had varnished sides and white roofs. Her bulwarks were white, her teak rail was varnished and her topsides were a very dark greeny-brown colour.

Floors and frames

Before floors can be replaced, the keelson has to be shifted. This will be bolted through the floors to the keel. The frames of most English fishing smacks are not checked into the keel but merely butt up to it. These frames are sometimes joined by short floors scarphed into them, or by heavy floors held up against them and sometimes side bolted to them. In taking out old frames it may be easier to make a template of their shapes before removing them. They can then be chiselled and cut out in small pieces. New frames can either be cut from grown crooks, which are hard to come by, or cut from $\frac{3}{4}$ in. marine ply and laminated. This last method was used by Bryan Thomas in his conversion of the big Colchester smack *Shamrock*.

Stem and apron

In the case of a damaged stem, frayed hood ends or an apron with rot in it, one method is to take out the old apron, fit a new apron and fasten the ends of the planks to this. Then remove the old stem and cut off the plank ends flush with the front of the apron and fit a new stempost overlapping the apron by the thickness of the planking, thus providing a rabbet for the hood ends. Charles Harker used this method when he had to give his smack *Iris* a new stem and apron.

Planks and sheer strakes

If these have to be replaced, it is easier to use freshly felled timber. The planks can then be pulled into position with tackles and cramps. To fasten them to the frames, drill and countersink and drive home flat point iron nails.

33 *Shamrock*, showing unobtrusive deckhouses

Decks

If the deck is very worn, the proper thing is to remove all the planks and any deck beams that look at all suspect, then replace beams and re-deck with $1\frac{1}{2}$ in. or 2 in. fir. This is of course a costly job and a reasonable alternative is to level off the old deck planks and cover with $\frac{3}{4}$ in. marine ply and then fibreglass this. The marine ply will act in the manner of a series of lodging knees and will stiffen the boat up considerably. It is no good putting fibreglass straight onto the old decking for there would be much too much movement in the deck for the fibreglass to adhere properly to it.

Caulking

Before you can start caulking, you must have a 12 in. caulking mallet and one or two caulking irons to drive in the oakum or cotton, a seam brush for painting the insides of the seams, and a caulking wheel. The seams in carvel planking are V-shaped. In the case of the thick planking (2 in.) of fishing smacks, it is only necessary to chamfer for about half the thickness of the plank; the inboard ends should make a close fit. The seams should be filled almost to the outside with twisted strands of oakum or bights of cotton, then painted over with a seam brush and finally covered with a special seam filler (such as Seamflex), using a flat palette knife. The oakum or cotton is hammered home with a caulking iron and mallet. It should be driven into seams that are clean and freshly painted with white lead paint that has not yet dried. For planking that is less than $\frac{3}{4}$ in. thick candle wicking is laid straight along the seam and not hammered but rolled in under pressure from the caulking wheel.

Caulking is a tricky job and if possible you should get the help of a shipwright, or at least watch one at work before undertaking any actual caulking yourself.

Steam bending
For steaming heavy timbers, a proper steam box is necessary. This can be improvised from an old cylindrical household boiler or water tank and will have to have one open end. Chock the tank up at an angle, half fill it with water and place a heater underneath it. When the water has been brought to boiling point your timber can be placed inside and the end of the tank blocked up with sacking. Keep the fire going and about an hour and a half should be enough to allow the steam to penetrate the wood. A rough-and-ready guide for the length of time to make timber pliable is to allow one hour of steaming time for every square inch of the cross-section of the timber.

Sometimes it is advisable to steam and bend timbers before fitting into a boat. *Boadicea*'s shelves were done in this way, by steaming them and then bending them round and fastening them with cramps to the *outside* of the boat. They were left in that position for some months and were then inserted into the boat through an opening in the stern, where the transom planks had been removed. When bending wood the annular rings in the grain should be at right angles to the way the bend goes, that is, they should curve towards the inside of the bend.

Scribing
This is the method of transferring with a divider or compass the curve or shape from an existing plank or timber to either a template or the new replacement plank or timber. The replacement timber or template is offered up to the original plank or timber and is brought as near to the curve as possible. The compass is then opened up and kept at the horizontal and moved down the curve making a series of dots or a continuous line on the replacement timber. These dots or line should give the required curve to be cut, but you should saw outside the line so that any unfairnesses can be adjusted when it is offered up.

Planking

Wood swells when wet and shrinks when dry, and hardwoods shrink and swell less than softwoods. So, in planking a boat allowance must be made for these factors. This shrinking or swelling is most evident in the direction of the annular rings. All planking should be fastened with the annular rings curved downwards or inwards. The same thing applies to beams and timbers. This swelling of the timbers when they are wet helps a boat to take up and to give you a watertight hull. It also makes for jamming hatchways and floorboards that cannot be shifted! So in all joinery and cabinet work, allowances must be made for this. When using tongue-and-groove, always use planks with a mitre joint; this will stop the tongue-and-groove from lifting or buckling up.

Scarphing planks or timbers

In boat building one does not have butt joints. The scarph joint is made up with a 1 in 10 rise to the angle of the scarph. To avoid feather ends cut the end of the scarph to not less than $\frac{3}{16}$ in., glue the surfaces together and through-fasten with staggered fastenings (staggered otherwise the timber may split). Hervey Garrett Smith* shows a fairly foolproof method of cutting plank scarphs so that both planks are cut at exactly the same angle. In his book he illustrates a simple jig, which is made up from a 2 in. plank slightly wider than the plank you will be scarphing and two $\frac{3}{4}$ in. thick oak side pieces which will act as guides for the plane. These side pieces, which need to be 3 or 4 inches deep, must have true, straight edges. Each side piece must be marked at say 8 in. from the end; the plank must have its ends cut off square and the side pieces can then be nailed to it, making an angle of 5° with the 8 in. marks coinciding with the end of the plank. The jig can then be mounted between two sawing benches and nailed to them so that it will not move. The planks to be scarphed can first have their scarphs cut to the approximate angle with a ripsaw and then be clamped into position on the jig. They can now be planed down to the exact angle of the scarph. When both planks are completed they can be glued up, using cramps.

The windlass

The barrel windlass used on smacks and bawleys is nearly always taken out by converters in favour of some kind of patent anchor winch. I think this is a great mistake; it is probably done from a misconception that these old windlasses are slow and difficult to use. In fact they are very much more

Boat Carpentry, H. G. Smith. Van Nostrand, New Jersey

34 *Shamrock*, deadeye and lanyards, not
rigging screws. In foreground note
horse for staysail tack block

powerful than any of their substitutes. They look right and the flat ringing
tone of the pawl on the iron teeth of the barrel is a harmonious noise. Very
considerable leverage can be obtained on the windlass handles and one can
stand up to work them. The anchor chain has to be fleeted away every so
often, but that is not difficult. The heaviest fisherman anchor can be
brought up to within an inch or two of the fairlead and, with the stock
across the bows, a bight of rope is dropped over the after fluke, which is
then hauled up to the rail and catted in that position.

Anchors
A heavy fisherman anchor of 150 lbs would hold the smack *Shamrock*
better than a 112 lb. CQR. For light weather a 56 lb. CQR, normally used as
the kedge anchor, would hold her perfectly well.

Deck paint
An alternative to *Shamrock*'s stone-coloured decks would be to do as was
done with *Boadicea*, and use the boat-builder William Wyatt's personal
mixture of raw linseed oil and red ochre which took two weeks to dry.

TEN

The flat-bottomed boats
of the Netherlands

Holland is the only maritime country in Europe that seems to be able to live in the twentieth century, yet to appreciate the values of the past. The use of the types of boat that belong to a tradition that goes back at least to the sixteenth century is a telling example of this attitude. The shallow steep seas and the wind-whipped waters of the Zeeland estuaries, the Zuider Zee and the Wadden Zee have produced a variety of idiosyncratic craft that can still be seen fishing, even if they are under power, and can still be seen sailing as yachts. And many more yachts have been built on the lines of these traditional craft. The botters, the boeiers, the tjalks, the hoogaars, the lemsteraaks, the hengsts and various other local types are uniquely suitable for these shallow waters, and for grounding out on estuary mudbanks and hard sandy beaches. Their rig, usually with a little curved gaff and steeving bowsprit, fits them perfectly. Fit a modern bermudan rig to one of these old boats and she would hardly move! The fact that many of these craft, both working and pleasure, are now built of steel rather than oak hardly lessens their charm. The rounded shapes and sweeping lines seem to come just as fair in steel plate as in timber and may well be a better proposition for the converter. Timbers that may be seventy years old are usually pretty sodden. These old-type shallow draught boats offer much in the way of conversion or restoration. What one has to be clear about, just as in the case of English fishing smacks, is just what they are suitable for when they are converted.

They are usually large enough to provide plenty of accommodation. They are ideal for sailing in shallow waters, and equally ideal for grounding on sandbanks. For relatively sheltered waters they can hardly be beaten as a floating holiday home in which children can feel they are on a real ship and not in a chromium plated discotheque. The feeling of being wrapped round by a piece of living history is also very engaging. Having said that, they can cost a lot to maintain. This depends on whether they are sound and whether they are all brightly varnished or merely painted. And finally, they are not suitable for prolonged passage-making. Crossing the North Sea in settled weather is well within their capabilities, but a summer gale down Channel or in the Irish Sea is something they would be well advised not to attempt. They are, after all, flat-bottomed boats, and in a big sea, in spite of their weight, they could be knocked over, and unlike the keel yacht they might not come up again.

As to what type is most suitable for conversion, this is largely a matter of availability and taste. The botters, both from the Zuider Zee and the North Sea, are perhaps the most characterful, yet the hoogaars may be better sea boats and the boeiers more roomy. They are all fascinating in their various ways: even the steel scows with their square bows have an elegance. The Dutch are not frightened of curves. The converter should bear this in mind and avoid straight lines like the devil.

For anyone interested in Dutch craft, a visit to the Scheepvaartmuseum, Cornelis Schuystraat 57, Amsterdam, or the Zuider Zee Museum, Enkhuizen, on the Ijsselmeer are well worth while. Also a careful study of *Ronde en platbodem jachten* by Dr T. Huitema, published in Amsterdam by P. N. van Kampen & Zoon N.V., 1962, is a great help to any converter or restorer. Even though the book is in Dutch, the plans are all self-explanatory.

The hengst is one of these traditional Dutch fishing craft; it is in fact a smaller version of the hoogaars of the West Schelde. The hengst was mainly used for mussel gathering on the sand banks and mudflats of the East Schelde. It was also used for dredging in the oyster fisheries.

Elizabeth Josina is a typical if somewhat heavily built hengst. She was built in 1905–6 at Terneuzen, the small fortified town at the north end of the Ghent-Schelde canal. The whole of her working life was spent with one family called Schot, at Tholen. There have been Schots at Tholen for the past two centuries. They were originally part of a tribe of Aberdeen fishermen who came over to Zeeland in the seventeenth and eighteenth centuries. Tholen, incidentally, is the birthplace of Cornelius Vermuyden, who drained the English fens. *Elizabeth Josina* was named after the first owner's wife. In due course this Captain Schot handed her over to his son, who eventually, when he was nearly seventy, sold her to Cmdr Richard Horncastle, R.N.

Richard Horncastle had previously owned a Thames barge, but he felt that with a very young family he needed a rather smaller craft, but one that had still something of the character of his barge. This hengst is under 35 ft overall, and though very heavily constructed by the standards of almost any other craft of her size, let alone of a comparably sized yacht, she is a lot smaller and a lot more handy than any spritsail barge. Her ability to take the sands on her flat bottom, her roominess and high bulwarks, make her a marvelous playground for young children. The hengst is a handy sailer in sheltered waters and will go to windward under mainsail alone. *Elizabeth Josina* is at her worst, as might be expected, passage-making against a head sea.

When Richard Horncastle bought *Elizabeth Josina* she was still being worked as a mussel boat, but with a massive one-cylinder 15 h.p. hot-bulb Kromhout diesel and no sails. All her spars and gear were coated with a mixture of diesel oil and tar, which no doubt was a splendid protection and preservative. The first job was to clean off, by scraping and scrubbing, all this stuff and to remove the smell from about sixty years of mussel gathering. Scraping her down to the bare oak was considered, but she had so many tingles on her that this was abandoned. The first stage of her restoration took place at Tholen, where the boat yard of Duivendijk re-rigged her and fitted her with shrouds for the first time in her life, and much to the disgust of Captain Schot. These craft were originally sailed without any lateral support to their very massive masts. The Dutch fishermen think it better that all the strain should be taken by the spars and the huge tabernacle rather than to allow the topsides to be subjected to racking strains via the

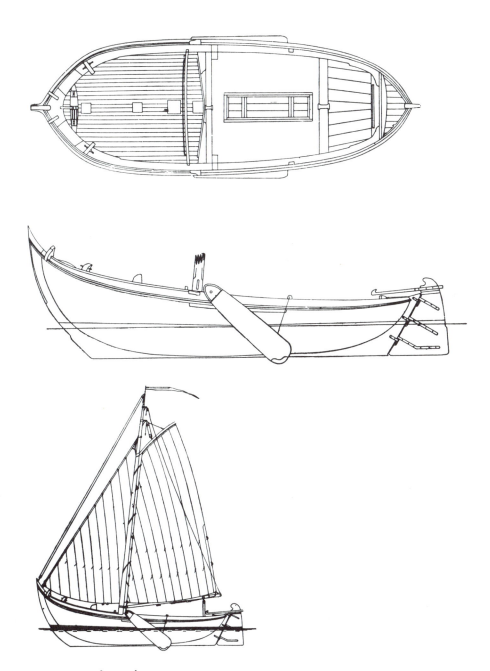

Fig. 111 Zuider Zee botter

Fig. 112 Boeier converted to a yacht

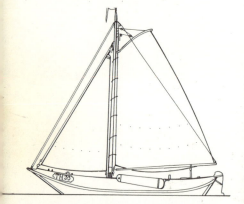

Fig. 113 Hoogaars from Tholen

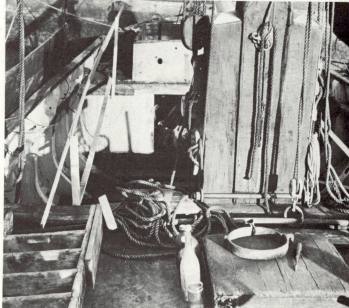

35 *Elizabeth Josina* after conversion

36 *Elizabeth Josina*, hengst from Tholen, before conversion

37 Foredeck, showing massive tabernacle

Fig. 114 Sail plan of hengst from Terneuzen

38 *Elizabeth Josina* afloat at Woodbridge after conversion

39 *Elizabeth Josina*, double bed and lavatory compartment

40 The dinette made up of church pews. The table slides down the pole to convert to a bed

41 Looking forward: entrance to foc's'le to port and the coal stove to starboard

42 *Wildcat*, converted botter under sail
(Beken)

chainplates. However Duivendijk, who knew more about restoring these craft than almost anyone else, said that she would be better with shrouds, so shrouds were fitted. Sails were made by Van Schneepen at Terneuzen. There was no sail plan. However, Van Schneepen and Duivendijk between them worked out what she would need. Her working rig is mainsail and staysail, with the bowsprit steeved. For passage-making or on a reach she flies a large jib from her bowsprit end. The working sails are of 20 oz. Egyptian cotton. No doubt they could have been made of flax, and would have been that much kinder to handle. The yard also fitted tackles to the leeboards to replace the single line by which they were raised and lowered. Her leeboards had been stored ashore for about thirty years, ever since she had been converted to motor power.

She was brought to England by her owner. On the first attempt she had to run back to Rotterdam, having weathered part of the storm tied up to the Goree light vessel. The vibration from the old Kromhout was so great that the alcohol in the compass frothed!

As soon as *Elizabeth Josina* reached her new home port of Woodbridge in Suffolk, work began on the conversion. The cleaning-up process was completed and the enormous Kromhout engine and the steel housing round it were removed. The hengst had been decked in forward from the stem to the after side of the mast to provide a cabin for the crew. Aft, she was decked to the fore side of the 'engine room.' This originally had a small hatch and must have been a storage hold.

The Kromhout was replaced by a second-hand 20 h.p. four-cylinder Britt marine engine, which is about as reliable as any petrol marine engine can be and about one-fifth the size of the old one-lung diesel. Then the building of the accommodation began.

This conversion is simple and appropriate. The original foc's'le cabin has been retained. It has been fitted up with two short bunks on either side for children, and a cot is suspended across the fore bulkhead just aft of the chain locker. In fact, as the foc's'le measures 6 ft fore and aft there will be room in it for two full-sized berths. Though the headroom is only 4 ft 4 in., the foc's'le at the after end and at deck level is 12 ft wide, so it is quite a roomy little cabin. The hatch, which could well have a Perspex lid, is 2 ft square, and is just forward of the tabernacle.

The 'engine room' was cleared to make the 5 ft long cockpit and side decks were put in. The cabin trunk is 12 ft 6 in. long with the forward end butting up against the after side of the tabernacle. It fills what was the fish well. The width of the cabin trunk is 6 ft 10 in. at the after end and 4 in.

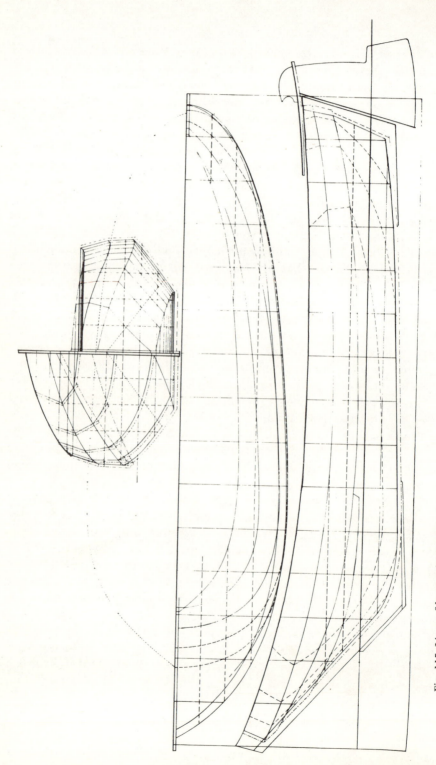

Fig. 115 Lines of hengst (T. Huitema)

The flat-bottomed boats of the Netherlands

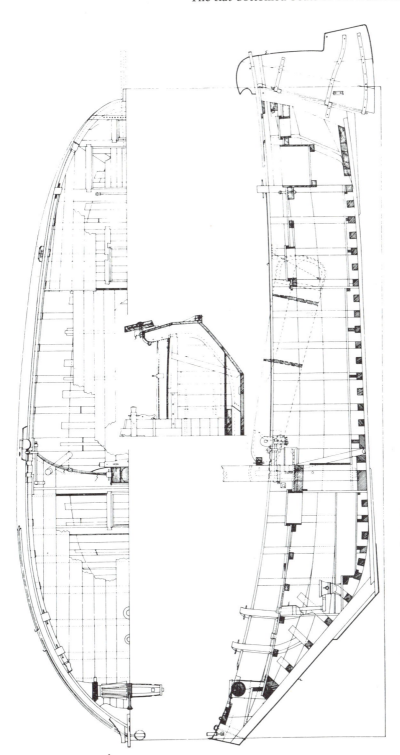

Fig. 116 Construction plan, elevation and section of hengst 11.20 m overall (T. Huitema)

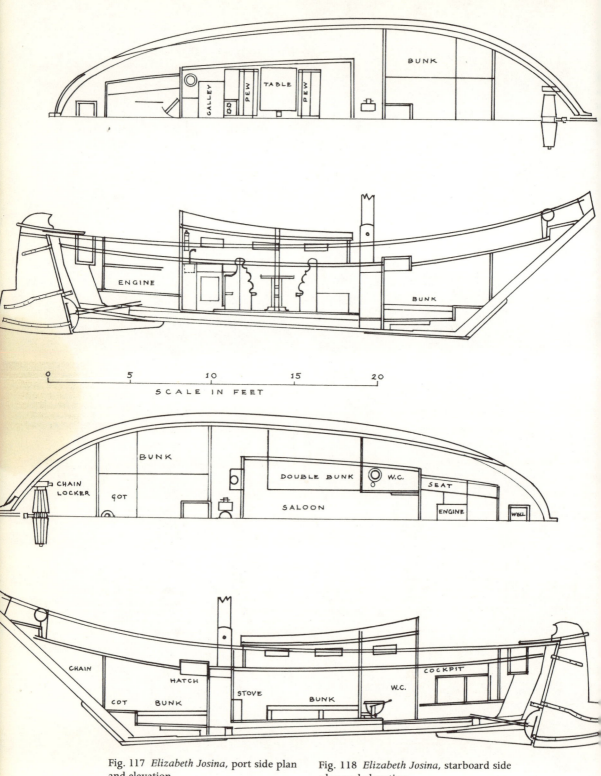

Fig. 117 *Elizabeth Josina*, port side plan and elevation

Fig. 118 *Elizabeth Josina*, starboard side plan and elevation

wider at the tabernacle. (The hengst is wider at the mast level than it is 12 ft aft, and the cabin trunk follows this line.) Richard Horncastle has given his cabin roof the proper Dutch curves. The sides of the cabin trunk are 2 ft high forward. The cabin trunk is planked and then covered in marine ply. It sweeps down in a concave curve to the fore end. In section it has an ogee curve with, in the centre, a 9 in. rise aft, flattening out to a $3\frac{1}{2}$ in. rise forward. The cockpit is quite roomy with the Britt engine sitting under a hinged flat-top 32 in. by 22 in. wide. There are wide benches ($13\frac{1}{2}$ in.) on either side of the cockpit and across the after end. The cockpit is enclosed within a coaming that sweeps down to the after end. As there is a drop of 3 ft from the seat level to the bottom of the cockpit, footrests have been fitted on either side of the engine box. Aft of the cockpit is the steering well, measuring 20 in. by 4 ft 3 in. wide. This looks like a baby's bath! It can be lifted out so that the stern gear can be reached. There is a further 3 ft of deck space aft of this. The cabin has folding doors with a 2 ft wide opening. One steps down 8 in. to the cabin sole where there is 6 ft 6 in. headroom. To port is the galley with a sink on the after bulkhead, and to starboard a roomy lavatory compartment with full standing headroom. Just forward of the galley is what yacht designers might call a 'dinette', but it is more like a confessional! With sublime ingenuity and also a sense of what is appropriate for such a massive vessel, Richard Horncastle has made up his dinette from two thoroughly Gothic church pews. In point of fact, it was one long oak pew, which he bought from a scrap merchant for about £4 and cut in half to make the two facing seats for the dinette. The double pew end also houses the gas stove. One end of the table slides down a vertical post to convert the dinette into a bed. On the opposite side of the cabin and forward of the lavatory compartment is a double bunk, which folds in half during the daytime. The forward end of the cabin has no bulkhead on the port side but merely a 3 ft 6 in. high opening into the foc's'le. In the centre of the fore end of the cabin are the 24 in. wide tabernacle beams and mast support. To starboard of this is an anthracite stove with a cupboard above it. Some Dutch tiles have been let into the front of the cupboard. Though this is a conversion carried out in England, *Elizabeth Josina* is still every bit a Dutchman's boat.

She has been sailed by her owner and his young family for several years, and though not at her best in heavy seas, has proved a splendid boat for sailing in the kind of waters for which she was intended. She has obviously earned the affection of her owner, who has said to me, 'What I would really like to do would be to clear away all my conversion efforts and put her back to the job for which she was built. We could do with a mussel fishery in East Anglia.'

ELEVEN

Scandinavian and Portuguese fishing boats for conversion

There are many types of Scandinavian fishing boats suitable for conversion. The Norwegian fishing boats which have been strongly influenced by the Colin Archer-designed pilot boats, though softwood built, are usually heavily framed and can make very roomy conversions. Mr Peter Bailey, who had formerly owned and restored a Colchester smack, searched the harbours of southern Norway before finding *Boan,* a prawning boat whose owner was having to sell because of ill health. *Boan* was built at Risør on the south coast of Norway in 1927. She shows the typical Colin Archer influence in her lines, though her stern is not as rounded as the true Colin Archer model. She is 35 ft overall, 13 ft 6 in. beam and draws 5 ft 6 in. She is heavily built of pine throughout, with 5 in.-sided grown frames fastened by tree nails. When Peter Bailey bought *Boan* she had a tall wheelhouse aft and a short mast, for she relied solely on her Rapp single cylinder hot-bulb diesel to drive her. Raahauge, the boatbuilder at Risør, surveyed her. As a result of his recommendations *Boan* was entirely re-decked, with three new deck beams and new hatch coamings. New horn timbers were fitted and new bulwarks and capping rails. In place of the main fish hatch a very neat 14 in. high coach roof was fitted, with a sliding hatch to port. This coach roof is only 5 ft 6 in. long by 5 ft 4 in. wide and barely shows above the bulwarks. At the forward end of the coach roof there is a small opening skylight, the lights protected with bronze rods. The whole structure is beautifully proportioned and built with dovetailed corners and a narrow-planked roof.

On the foredeck, the small square hatchway, which is set slightly to port, was replaced with a curved-back scuttle. This has folding doors and the curved roof hinged backwards. An interesting feature is that the anchor follows big-ship practice and is housed in a hawsepipe.

Raahauge also re-sparred the vessel with a very massive pine main mast and an elegantly tapered plank bowsprit, which is 14 in. wide at the inboard end. A self-draining cockpit was fitted in place of the wheelhouse.

There was not time to re-caulk the vessel before Peter Bailey and his crew set off for home. Through the overflooding of her cylinder with fuel her huge diesel ran amok. The fearful vibration caused the boat to shed some of her caulking and also to fracture her fuel line. They were just able to make the entrance to the Thuberon canal. *Boan* very nearly sank before she could be slipped. Some temporary re-caulking was done and they started off again. However she was still leaking quite badly, but the pump, driven by the engine, was just able to keep pace with the inflow of water. Fifty miles off the island of Sylt, the cooling system on the engine failed, and in order to prevent it heating up they had to cut their power. They ran for the river Ems, but only by bailing with buckets as well as pumping were they able to keep pace with the leaks. They reached Delfzyl and here *Boan* was lifted out of the water, satisfactorily re-caulked and the engine repaired. That was the end of their troubles and they reached the Blackwater quite safely. She now lies in a very snug mud berth at the head of Peldon creek and her conversion continues.

The heavy one-lung motor is now being replaced by a rather more amenable piece of machinery, a three-cylinder Lister diesel. No fitting out had been done below decks, but a double bunk is planned in the roomy forepeak. Just forward of the mast is the coal stove and on either side of the

Scandinavian and Portuguese fishing boats for conversion

43 *Boan*, built at Risør, in Norway, in 1927, before conversion

44 *Boan*: the first thing to come off was the wheelhouse

45 *Boan* after conversion

46 Deck view forward before conversion

47 After conversion. Note inboard end of plank bowsprit, divided to come either side of stem post

48 Fife rail, fore end of deckhouse with skylight

49 New curved-back scuttle over forehatch. Top hinges back

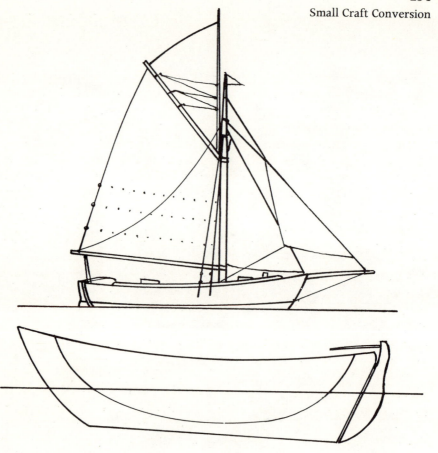

Fig. 119 The Colin Archer influence in
her lines

main saloon will be bunks with benches inboard of these. *Boan*'s 13 ft 6 in.
beam and much higher freeboard than the English smacks allows plenty of
scope for accommodation.

Aft of the cockpit, there will be a large water tank and fuel tanks will be
fitted on each side of the cockpit. When *Boan*'s conversion is completed, she
should make a beautiful little ship. Fit to go anywhere, she yet retains
much of the character of the fishing boat she had once been.

The completed cost of such a conversion would work out at only about a
third of the cost of building such a boat.

There are one or two builders in Norway who will supply hulls for completion. The Hausberg Boatyard near Bergen produces a 30 ft wooden hull,
10 ft wide with a draught of 4 ft, which would make the basis of a very nice

little inshore trawler or a conventional cruising yacht. Another yard will build a hull very similar to *Boan*'s but to a higher specification, pine planked on oak frames, designed for owner-completion for £4000 ex yard (1971 price) including the engine.

If one can afford this starting price, it would seem to be a very good proposition. Whether buying a new hull or converting an old one, the Scandinavian boats have much to offer both in looks and in their roominess.

Marka is a 31 ft LOA by 9 ft 1 in. beam and 3 ft 6 in. draft Norwegian 'dory' converted into a motor-sailer. When Richard Riggs bought her she was lying at Woodbridge, Suffolk. She had been used as a service boat and was carried aboard the mother ship to one of the Norwegian fishing fleets. She did not look too promising a proposition, for her upper strakes were sheathed in steel plate and were in very poor condition. Both stem and stern posts were in need of at least partial replacement. She was battered and weatherworn, for she had never been painted. Her larch planks had been oiled, and perhaps once upon a time, varnished. Yet the lovely sweep of her lines and her pretty Colin Archer stern were very appealing and she was more than roomy enough to house the Riggs family.

The conversion was carried out at Woodbridge, by Frank Knights' boatyard to the plans of J. Francis Jones and Partners. When *Marka* was first chocked up in the building shed, her old hull looked so woe-begone that one of the apprentices chalked up a notice 'Restoration Appeal: Please Give Generously' and he placed an old tin chamber pot in front of the boat, as a receptacle for contributions.

When the conversion was complete, no doubt he had to eat his words, or drown them in the proceeds of his appeal for *Marka* was by that time a lovely little ship.

Marka was clinker (or lapstrake) built and iron-fastened with round-headed iron nails to grown frames. Her bottom planking and frames were sound but she lacked transverse floors. She had recently been fitted with a new 20 h.p. Saab diesel, which proved to be a faultless piece of machinery.

This conversion was planned by the owner for a specific purpose. Richard Riggs had sailed and cruised since he was a child, but he had come to the sensible conclusion that if he wanted to cruise with a very young family, something different from the average cruising sailing yacht or even motor sailer was needed. So he planned his conversion round a large mid-ships well, which allowed the young children plenty of scope for letting off steam, without any danger of their falling overboard. It also meant that their parents could sail the boat from a beautifully designed wheelhouse aft (this occupies what would have been a cockpit in a conventional design), without the children getting in the way.

The deck plan from forward consists of a small foredeck, for handling anchor and head sails, a long cabin trunk, the midships well, the wheelhouse and a small deck aft. The cabin, well and wheelhouse are all set inside side decks protected with stanchions and lifelines, which shows that this boat has been planned by someone used to handling boats at sea. These clear side decks are just as valuable for use in inland waterways, where one may have to hurry fore or aft, to fend off from a lock gate or cast off a warp.

When the conversion work started, it was found that the hull was basically sound, though she needed considerable re-fastening. The round-headed iron nails had to be shipped over from Norway. Floors were put in, doubling up on each frame. New sections were scarphed into the stem and sternposts and new sheer strakes were fitted. The thwarts were removed and deck beams and bulkheads combined with the new floors provided more than adequate stiffening. The boat was further strengthened by the use of $\frac{3}{4}$ in. marine ply for the deck. This marine ply was also used for bulkheads, the sides and top of the wheelhouse and cabin trunk.

Marka's most effective colour scheme is worth noting. The hull has red antifouling on the bottom, a white boot topping and for her topsides a rich dark green that the Dutch so often use for the front doors of the old houses (which her owner had seen in the old towns of the Zeeland estuaries). *Marka*'s sheer is emphasised by a wide varnished rubbing strake. Everything above deck level, that is, the sides and tops of the deck houses and the stanchions, is painted white, with brightwork for hatch covers, grab rails and the louvred slides to the cabin.

Marka's Saab diesel gives her ample power, but she is also sloop-rigged, with a loose footed gaff and a large headsail. Her Terylene sails are red ochre coloured and under this rig she will run and reach quite successfully. In her first season, *Marka* cruised up and down the East Coast and crossed the Channel to Calais. Wherever she went she excited much interest, as well she might, for she is a most characterful and sensible little family cruiser. At the time of writing, she is based on the Solway Firth and has proved just as successful in her new northern cruising grounds.

Portuguese inshore fishing boats as a basis for conversion

Sesimbra is a small fishing port, about 30 km south of Lisbon, lying in a wide semicircular bay, protected from the Atlantic by Cape Espichel. The

From left to right

50 *Marka*: new rubbing strakes have been fitted and a new top to the sternpost scarphed to the old one

52 Looking forward into cabin and WC compartment

54 *Marka* at sea. Note windscreen wiper

51 Stern: wheelhouse front and sides being offered up

53 Wheelhouse in position

55 *Marka*'s sweeping lines are emphasised by her pulpit and lifelines. The pulpit has excellent clearance for the handling of the anchor

56 Stern view of 22 ft Sesimbra fishing
boat, showing typical paint scheme

57 Sesimbra boats could make
characterful conversions

anchorage is quite secure unless the wind blows hard from the south-south-west. The local fishing boats are a most interesting feature of this area. They are all motor propelled, except for the very small pulling craft. The Ministry of Marine, at the beginning of the last war, had plans drawn up for various standard sizes, but how faithfully these lines are followed, I would not know. The boats are all built in the open air, sometimes in enclosed shipyards, sometimes on the beach or even beside the road, and planks and timbers are hand cut in open saw pits. The craft are iron fastened and carvel built of softwood, with red pine for the planking and timbers and eucalyptus for the keels.

The finish is fairly rugged and the expectation of hard-working life is about fifteen years. However, a very pretty little 6·70 metre craft (see plans) very heavily built and pretty beamy cost only 17,000 escudos a few years ago, complete except for the engine. The flaring bows, great sheer and elliptical sterns make excellent sea boats, which are colourful and practical.

Without too much alteration the Sesimbra boats would make very nice little knockabout motor-sailer, fishing or cruising boats. This would be a case for restraint over deckhouses: the example of some of the yacht versions of Scottish fishing boats should be a pretty salutary warning.

The colour schemes of the Sesimbra boat are of infinite variety. The heavy sheer and rubbing strakes are emphasised with bands of colour, perhaps black, mustard, vermilion and sage green, or other combinations, with tar or red antifouling below the waterline. Some have vertical stripes painted on their rounded sterns, a vestigial reminder of stern and quarter galleries. On either side of the bow there may be painted an eye, a cross, or a star, and sometimes other decorations, such as a yellow spiny fishbone on the deep blue topsides of one handsome boat, which, like so many others, had a stempost towering at least a couple of feet above the bulwarks and surmounted by a red muffin-shaped knob. The names of these boats encompassed the whole saintly calendar and the names of all the fishermen's wives, uncles and aunts as well. The *Dedicacio* rubbed shoulders with *Deus Te* and *Joaquin Filipe*; plain *Suzette* with the *Calgodonar* and *Familia Parada*; the *Curiosidada* with the *Eliza Rodrigues*. It was a glorious sight to see several hundred of these colourful little boats bobbing about in the bay. They landed their catches at the top of the tide and then, as the ebb set in, they would lay their fish out in ordained patterns on the hard clean sand, to await the tax men. The first time we saw this happen was after dark. The beach was lit by dozens of flaring torches. After the fish was taxed it was loaded into panniers carried by extremely patient (and well cared for) donkeys. The sombre clothes and dark eager faces of the fishermen lit by the flickering light of the torches made a scene of very great attraction, that might have happened on any night during the last two thousand years.

The fish were of many varieties. There was a curious carp-like fish, fat and round, that was always displayed on a separate little pillow of sand, there were piles of sardines and 'ladders' of esparda, a long swordblade of a fish that is most delicious. These they twisted in pairs into figures of eight, loading them into flat trays on the donkeys. There were conger eels and barrels of octopus and squid. On every tide this bountiful harvest was laid out in the same manner.

All day long the fishermen would sit in the shade of the houses, baiting up their lines or mending their nets. The seine nets are of gigantic proportions and they needed as many as eighty men, forty a side, to carry them ashore or back to the boats, and it was manpower for everything. Though it was swelteringly hot, we never saw a fisherman stripped to the waist.

The Portuguese must be the finest handlers of pulling boats and small craft anywhere in the world. I remember seeing other Portuguese fishermen at Camera da Lobos in Madeira landing their boats through wild surf on a steep-shelving beach. And the performance of the Portuguese dorymen on the Newfoundland Banks is legendary.

I visited several of the boatyards (or boatbuilding sites) and later learnt a little by watching the shipwrights at work. I learnt rather more one evening when the proprietor of one of the yards and his son joined me in the bar of my hotel, and over glasses of excellent Portuguese brandy we discussed fishing and the building of fishing boats in a mixture of Portuguese, French and Dumb Crambo. The motor fishing vessels have, naturally enough, developed from local types of sailing craft, but I failed to find any plans or models or pictures showing these boats under sail.

With some additional depth to their keels and by blocking up the large propeller gap in the deadwoods these boats can be converted to sail, but they obviously make better motor fishing vessels with auxiliary sail.

I have taken a standard Sesimbra fishing boat and worked out a possible conversion. Though she is only 22 ft overall, she has a beam of 8 ft 9 in. and with her full bilges and almost flat bottom amidships has a depth from the top of her bulwarks to the floorboards of 3 ft 6 in., so the cabin trunk need only stick up 1 ft above the bulwarks to give reasonable sitting headroom. One should remember E. F. Knights' philosophic remark, 'If one wishes to assume an erect position, one can go on deck.'*

* *The Falcon on the Baltic*, E. F. Knight, Adlard Coles Ltd, 1951

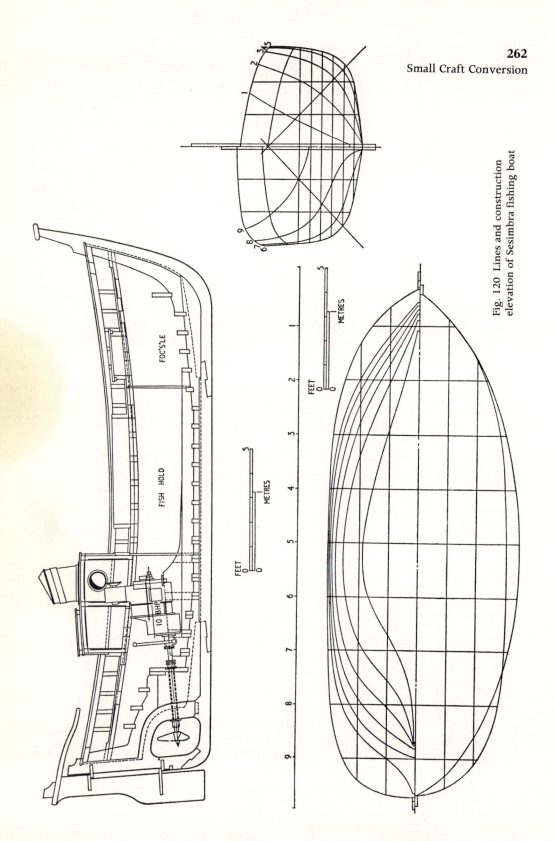

FOC'S'LE

FISH HOLD

10 BHP

FEET
METRES

FEET
METRES

Fig. 120 Lines and construction
elevation of Sesimbra fishing boat

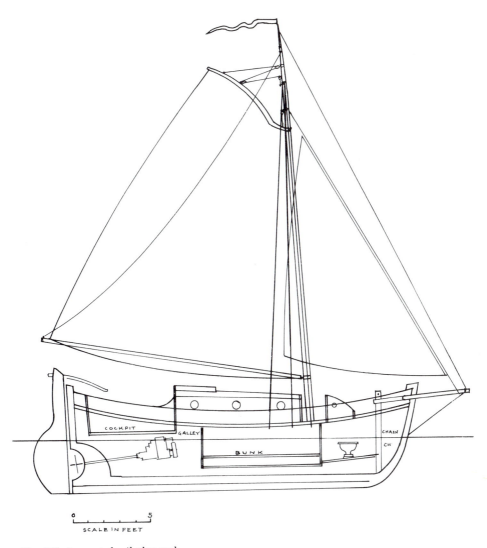

COCKPIT GALLEY

BUNK

CHAIN
CH.

0   5
SCALE IN FEET

Fig. 121 Suggested sail plan and
conversion for Sesimbra fishing boat

The actual depth below her decks is not much more than 2 ft and below the main hatch just over 3 ft. This hatch is 4 ft 6 in. long and about the same width, so if the conversion is to be kept to its simplest, the cabin trunk could be limited to this size, making use of the hatch coamings. The engine house could remain as it is, though the funnel shown on this plan was not visible on many of the boats. If the engine was an air-cooled diesel, the funnel could serve as an outlet for the hot air.

For an auxiliary sailing cruiser, I think this little boat would benefit by at least another 6 in. on her keel with the full depth aft and tapering up to the forefoot. The propeller gap in the deadwood would need filling in and a gap cut in the sternpost for the propeller. This of course would need a longer shaft. The rudder could be given rather more area and carried down to the depth of the false keel.

A gaff sloop rig would be the best proposition for the hull, and I think the traditional Dutch rig with a short curved gaff would match the rounded lines of this Sesimbra boat. To get any area into the fore triangle, one would have to fit a bowsprit. This should poke through the bulwarks, fishing boat fashion, on the starboard side. In this case the attractive upstanding bun-topped stempost would have to be cut down, otherwise it would interfere with the headsail when going about.

For a motor fishing vessel conversion with auxiliary sail, the simplest thing would be to have a dipping lugsail, set well inboard. In this case there would be no boom to get in the way if one were handling a trawl, and would leave the foredeck clear.

The kind of approach outlined here could be applied to many different types of boat in different parts of the world. I think the essential thing, and this applies to all conversions, is to keep as near as possible to the original character of the boat.

In the case of these Portuguese boats, they are such pretty little craft there is every reason for keeping them as near to the original as possible. Their colour schemes I have mentioned above. For the auxiliary sloop conversion, I think it would be just possible to fit a lavatory under the fore-hatch and give sitting headroom by converting the hatch into a semi-circular scuttle. It would not look inappropriate. The cabin would occupy the space of the original fish hold, which is 7 ft long and the full width of the ship.

The engine I have left as it is: a hefty one-lung diesel. If a hull like this was bought without an engine, a more compact unit could be installed, when the engine house could be removed and a longer 8 ft trunk fitted. The essential thing about these very characterful little hulls is to keep them looking like little ships. It is inappropriate, in fact futile, to try and make them into a so-called modern yacht. For their size, they are heavy displacement craft. A bermudan rig would be quite useless for such a hull.

TWELVE

Miscellaneous items

Wheelhouses and cockpit shelters

The virtue of a wheelhouse in sailing cruisers as well as in motor vessels was sharply underlined for me whilst cruising on the West Coast of Scotland in the two seasons before this book was published. After a chilly, windblown, wet cruise across the North Sea to the Zeeland estuaries in *Patient Griselda,* my little Dutch-rigged gaff cutter, I decided something ought to be done for the helmsman and crew before we sailed north for the Western Isles. I first of all considered a folding hood, but as my cockpit was separated from the cabin by a wide bridge deck, a temporary shelter of this sort presented some difficulties. If there is no bridge deck separating cabin from cockpit, it is quite a simple matter to fit a folding hood over the sliding hatch or to build a permanent doghouse which would give some shelter and protection from rain and spray. This is what Mr Stan Smyth of Wareham, Hampshire did with his Debutante, incidentally greatly improving the look of the craft. It was while I was pondering on these problems that I came across a letter from Mr Smyth about small boat shelters in *Yachts and Yachting*, March 1969. Mr Smyth's letter is worth quoting:

Having been associated with small boat sales for many years and writing with some experience of the extreme discomfort one has to put up with at sea, in particular the cold wet misery that we so often endure offshore during our English summer, I now ask, when is some enterprising builder going to offer reasonable weather protection in a small sailing boat? Without exception motor cruisers, even runabouts, are normally completed with windscreens, although from observation the average time afloat varies from a few minutes to an hour or so. Compared with the long passages undertaken by small sailing cruisers where total exposure to the elements has to be endured for ten, fifteen or twenty hours at a stretch, this lack of even elementary protection becomes difficult to understand or accept. My own Debutante was converted last winter by the addition of a miniature wheelhouse shelter giving sitting headroom. This was done carefully to scale, the boat's appearance being greatly enhanced. This shelter extends over approximately half the cockpit area so that one has the alternative of sitting out in the open on the rare occasions when this is acceptable.

In practice the advantages are enormous, one can now sit in comparative silence, *in ordinary clothing,* out of the wind and spray, enjoying the passage rather than enduring it. In harbour the cabin access can be left open for ventilation without fear of rain getting below.

Charts and navigation gear such as hand compass, binoculars, etc. can be handled easily, food can be eaten in comfort, electrical gear, torches and radio can be readily available without fear of swamping; in short, a very great boon and blessing. To my mind this feature, universal on large motor sailers, should be demanded by all small boat owners who intend undertaking long cruises.

I later discussed this shelter with Mr Smyth. Debutantes have a very marked camber to their decks, and there is a break between cabin top and side decks. To get the lines and appearance right a great deal of messing about with cardboard templates was needed. This preliminary trial and error work is essential in any alteration to a boat of this kind; in fact it is necessary in any conversion, especially when planning cabin tops and wheelhouses.

For this sort of work, the geometry is somewhat involved and extensive drawings and plans are needed so that templates can be made to work out the most acceptable angles. For the Debutante's doghouse, after the templates had been made, two front panels and two side panels were cut from $\frac{5}{16}$ in. marine ply. To these panels, frames of 3 in. by 1 in. were fitted, overlapping where it was necessary to allow for bevels. The two front panels were placed exactly on the line of the original washboard so that the hatchway ended up completely inside the wheelhouse. These panels were screwed and glued to each other at the centreline and to a shaped 'stempiece' and also to the deck. Side panels were now fitted which had quite marked tumblehome. They were joined to the front panels and the side decks. In order to have an unbroken deckhead an *external* beam was planned for the rear of the doghouse, so in order to fit the roof, a temporary beam had to be positioned underneath. The fore and aft beam is also external and both these beams serve as hand rails. The object of all this is to give one a smooth deckhead without any beams against which one could bang one's head.

As the roof had been designed with a deep camber, it was made up of two *thin* sheets ($\frac{1}{4}$ in.) of marine ply to facilitate considerable bending. The roof was made to overlap all the way round so that rain and spray would run off it. The windows were of $\frac{3}{4}$ in. Perspex. Hardboard templates were made for these, and very accurately made, for Perspex is expensive stuff. The windows were edged with $\frac{1}{2}$ in. alloy beading, both to give a good appearance and to save wear on the edges of the Perspex. Here one should use alloy screws to avoid corrosion.

All the ply edges were covered with beading which was glued and pinned. This is most important; otherwise delamination in the ply is bound to happen as soon as water begins to soak in through the uncovered edges. The final structure is very strong and the roof will stand a man's weight.

The hatch cover was made to slide and was usually stowed away when the boat was in use. The deck area inside the shelter provided a useful shelf. The cost of materials for the operation was about £20, the plywood and the Perspex being the main items.

The wheelhouse for *Patient Griselda* was in many ways a simpler piece of construction, but aesthetically was a much tougher problem than the design for the shelter on the Debutante, which is a typical small, modern, reverse sheer yacht. As Mr Smythe says, 'the doghouse greatly improved her rather bald look.' *Patient Griselda* is quite a different sort of craft. She has a sweeping sheer with marked Dutch characteristics, with a very pretty ogee hollow curved cabin top. As she has a bridge deck it was virtually impossible to join the shelter to the cabin, so it had to become a separate structure. Because of the character of this boat it seemed to me that the best thing was to make this shelter as like a fishing boat's wheelhouse as possible.

The wheelhouse, as we first built it, was designed to the shape of the cockpit with its sides bolted to the cockpit coamings. As the cockpit tapered aft from a width of 4 ft at the forward end to 3 ft aft, the wheelhouse followed this shape. This made a rather ugly structure with a fair amount of windage on its wide, flat, forward end. After a couple of years use when, in spite of its unattractive appearance, it had more than proved its worth both as a complete shelter when under power or as a spray breaker when sailing, I redesigned it, reducing the width forward to the same width as it was aft

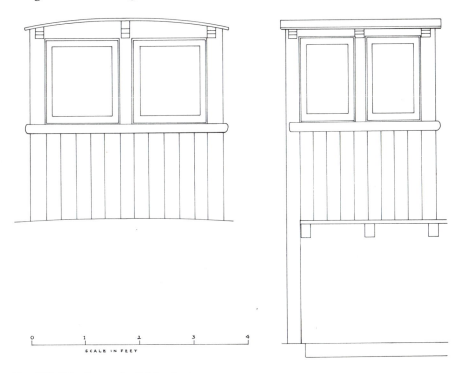

SCALE IN FEET

0   1   2   3   4

Fig. 122 Wheelhouse for fishing boat, front and side elevations

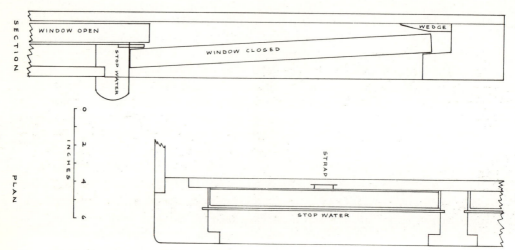

Fig. 123 Details of wheelhouse windows

(3 ft 1 in.). The new design was largely based on *Silver Darling*'s wheelhouse (page 271). Its fore and aft measurement was reduced to allow for more room for the helmsman, who when sailing the ship sits on the side deck aft of the shelter. When he is steering the boat under power he can stand in the shelter. Though we refer to this shelter as a wheelhouse, we have so far not fitted a wheel. If we ever did we should still retain the tiller for use when sailing.

The forward end of the wheelhouse is rounded, which greatly adds to its appearance and also seems to match the Dutch curves of the cabin top. The front windows are made to open. They are the old-fashioned railway carriage type. When closed, the windows slope backwards and the bottom of each window rests on the sill, on the outside of a half-inch high strip of brass which acts as a stopwater. When opening the windows they are lifted up by a strap over this stopwater and then lowered into a recess. It is a most simple piece of construction and completely effective. The after end of the wheelhouse is open, but can be closed with a canvas curtain which is normally rolled up and clipped into position at the deck head.

If this wheelhouse was going onto an open boat, such as a 26 ft fishing lifeboat conversion, the after end would be closed with an 18 in. wide door in the starboard side (see Chapter 8).

The windows in the first wheelhouse were protected by two horizontal bronze rods. This protection was mainly against bangs from such things

58 Debutante *Dipper* with doghouse, which greatly improves her looks

59 Front view of doghouse

60 Wheelhouse on *Silver Darling*, a converted Falmouth gig

61 Front view of wheelhouse. Note that it has old fashioned 'railway carriage' style opening windows

62 Wheelhouse on 6 ton cutter. Note bronze bars across the over-large windows, as a protection against bangs from fuel cans, etc.

as heavy fuel cans. It also added to the appearance. On the new wheel-house there is a varnished mahogany grab rail on either side of the roof and a folding carved boom support to the port side. This boom support is not in the centre as the boom would then come immediately over the centre of the cabin hatchway.

A lot of thought went into the design of this little box, both to make it a useful shelter and to make it look as if it really was part of the ship. The greatest difficulty was in the smallness of this boat, for she is only 24 ft 6 in. overall. If she had been 32 ft or more there would have been much less of a problem about scale.

Lavatories

Boat lavatories vary in price, type and size. They differ from land-based loos in the use of pumps and valves to get rid of excreta and to draw in sea-water for flushing. It is possible to get both these operations executed by one single pump, though the double pump WC such as the Baby Blake is in very wide use. Fitting a WC into a boat is a job for a plumber if lead pipes are used. Today, however, frequent use is made of reinforced corrugated plastic hose. This makes the job of installation relatively easy for the amateur. In either case, the effluent pipe must be shaped into a loop well above the waterline. This is to prevent water siphoning back into the boat, should the valves fail.

The smallest WCs, such as the Lavac (height $8\frac{3}{4}$ in., depth $15\frac{1}{2}$ in., width $14\frac{1}{2}$ in.) or the Simpson Lawrence 400 (height 10 in., depth $19\frac{1}{2}$ in., width $16\frac{1}{2}$ in.) can be fitted into quite confined spaces. For inland waterways chemical closets are obligatory. For cruising *at sea* in quiet places, away from crowds, there is nothing more hygienic than a bucket!

Coal stoves

In the first London Boat Show of the 1970s, as far as I could see, there was not a single boat fitted with a coal stove. This must be symptomatic of something. Either yachtsmen do not feel the cold any more, or they only sail in midsummer, or in a more temperate climate than that in which I usually find myself.

The difference a coal stove can make to the enjoyment of a sailing holiday, or at least the endurance of one as far as my crew was concerned, was brought home to me (on the West Coast of Scotland) in the wild-wet summer of 1970. However damp and cold and miserable it was outside, inside, the cabin of our boat was as dry and snug as a bread-oven. Also, a heating stove increases the sailing season by some months. The type of bogie stove we use is similar to the kind made for use in caravans. It is coated with vitreous enamel and is only 17 in. high and $11\frac{1}{2}$ in. square. It burns smokeless fuel—in fact it will burn almost anything except those awful little ovals made from coal dust and cement—mainly cement, from my experience.

The only disadvantage that this stove has is that the chimney comes out of the top and one cannot boil a kettle on it. There used to be a dear little cast-iron stove called a Caledonia Dumpy which was only 8 in. square and had its chimney coming out of the back, and an opening on the top for cooking. It was manufactured by Lane Girvan Ltd of Baybridge in Scotland.

A stove that one can cook on is the Nipper, which is 21 in. high and 13 in. deep and $21\frac{1}{2}$ in. wide, or with a hot plate extension, $25\frac{1}{2}$ in. wide. It is a proper little cooking range. It has two hot plates and an oven $9\frac{1}{2}$ in. wide, $10\frac{1}{2}$ in. deep and $7\frac{1}{2}$ in. high. It weighs 101 lbs so would only be suitable for boats with room to spare.

This stove and a closed bogie stove called the Albermarle, the same dimensions as the one mentioned above, are both supplied by Captain O. M. Watts Ltd, 49 Albemarle St, London W1. Simpson Lawrence Ltd, St Andrews Sq., Glasgow C1 supply through the trade a little bogie stove called the Tor Gem and also stove funnels, including one with the Liverpool head and deck flanges, etc.

The installation of a coal stove calls only for common sense. The stove should not be nearer than 3 in. to any wooden bulkhead, and if nearer than 9 in. the bulkhead should have a sheet of asbestos screwed to the front of it, with a $\frac{3}{4}$ in. air gap between the asbestos and the surface of the wood. The stove funnel should be lagged if it passes through any bulkhead, and it should pass through the deck via a flanged socket or even an outer chimney. I have the latter arrangement on my boat and I believe it helps the fire to draw. This may be due to the inner chimney not being cooled as soon as it gets through the deck. The double chimney projects about 9 in. above and below the deck. The stove funnel fits onto the above-deck part and can be taken off and stowed below when the fire is not in use. A circular hardwood plate is then screwed down onto the open top of the double chimney.

The tender

A small cruiser's tender is a problem indeed. If you intend to go cruising at sea, you must have a dinghy that will stow on deck. This will have to be a pram, about 7 ft long, of spruce or GRP (for lightness), or a folding canvas

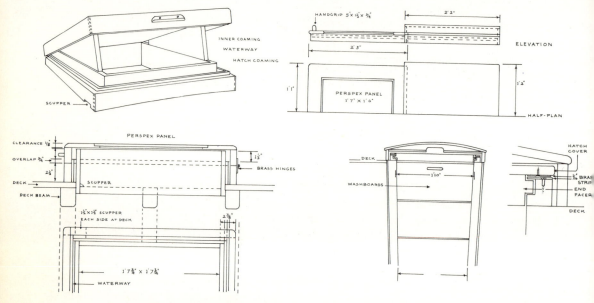

Fig. 124 Leakproof hatches. Designs by
Maurice Griffiths G.M.

dinghy, or an inflatable boat such as that made by the Avon Rubber Co.
And you will have to consider where you are going to stow it before you
start your conversion. On our 26 ft lifeboat ketch we could have stowed a
small pram on the foredeck, or a folding dinghy on the side deck. For ease of
stowing, an inflatable dinghy wins every time. Though they are slow boats
to row, they are very stable and safe. In emergencies they can be used as a
liferaft.

If you merely intend to potter about rivers and estuaries you can tow
your dinghy, and there is no need to worry about stowing it on deck. It can
usefully be a 9 ft or 10 ft dinghy, possibly fitted with a centreboard, short
mast and lugsail. The mast and spars should be short enough to stow inside
the boat.

Leak-proof hatches
Maurice Griffiths designed a double-coaming hatch in 1936 which over the
years has been modified slightly. This is the only hatch that I know that
really keeps out the sea. Eric Hiscock fitted one in his *Wanderer III* and
found it completely satisfactory. The designer's drawing (Fig. 124) makes
the construction very clear. The essence of the design lies in the double

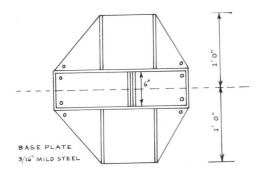

BASE PLATE
3/16" MILD STEEL

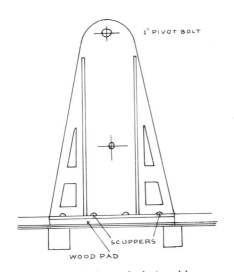

1" PIVOT BOLT

SCUPPERS

WOOD PAD

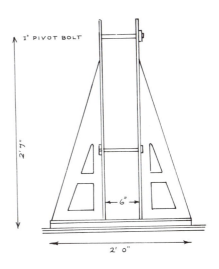

1" PIVOT BOLT

Fig. 125 Steel tabernacle designed by
J. Francis Jones and Partners

coamings. The Perspex panel in the top is, of course, optional. If light is not needed below, the top can be made up of marine ply. The timber can be mahogany, teak or iroko and the dimensions can be adjusted to fit the boat, except for the clearance and the minimum inside measurement of 1 ft 7¾ in. square.

Sliding hatches
This design, also by Maurice Griffiths, shows as near a leakproof sliding hatch as one can get. An interesting point in this drawing is the tapered

63 Wheelhouse on Bergen trawler

64 Wheelhouse on *Scarbh*, Scottish MFV beautifully converted to a motor-sailer

65 Spray hood on Neptune class yacht, which has the advantage of being removable

slides (or washboards) which serve in place of folding doors. Tapered thus, they are much less likely to jam.

Tabernacle

J. Francis Jones designed this tabernacle for an 8-ton sloop. It is welded in $\frac{3}{16}$ in. mild steel plate. Though not shown in the drawing a fife rail of $\frac{1}{4}$ in. thick by $1\frac{1}{2}$ in. wide mild steel strap could be welded on to the web stiffeners and $\frac{3}{8}$ in. holes could be drilled for $8\frac{1}{2}$ in. long steel rod, which could act as belaying pins. The tabernacle in the drawing measures 2 ft 7 in. from deck to pivot bolt. For smaller craft such as the 26 ft lifeboat, this could be reduced by at least 9 in. in height.

Glossary

Glossary

A-bracket: a two-armed strut fitted to one side or the other of the sternpost and forward of it, to carry the propeller shaft.

Adze: a tool like an axe with the blade set at right angles to the handle and curving towards it.

Anchor: bower, the main or heavier anchor.

CQR, a ploughshare-shaped anchor.

Danforth, a double-bladed anchor with a pivoted head, superficially like the anchors used by large ships.
kedge, the second anchor, approximately two-thirds the weight of the bower anchor.

Apron: a backing or strengthening timber inside the stempost.

Auger bit: a bit with a long spiral cutting edge.

Auger, bull-nosed: a solid-nosed auger

Backstay: a wire stay which prevents the mast from falling forward.

Ball-peen hammer: a hammer with a rounded head used for burring the end of copper nails over the rooves when fastening planks.

Barge-yacht: a small flat-bottomed sailing vessel, fitted with leeboards.

Bawley: the name probably derives from 'boiler' and is applied to shrimpers from Harwich and Leigh-on-Sea. These boats carried boilers for cooking the shrimps.

Bawley rig: the distinctive features are the large topsail, the very long gaff and the absence of a boom.

Bermudan: type of rig with a triangular fore and aft sail.

Bilge: the curve of the hull where topsides and bottom planks meet, also the space inside the vessel below the floorboards.

Bilge keel: a projecting fore and aft fin or plank on edge, fastened to the outside of the bilge planks.

Bitts: timbers set on or through the foredeck for belaying the anchor cable or mooring rope.

Bobstay: chain or wire from the end of the bowsprit to the stempost.

Boot-topping: a strip of different coloured paint along and above the waterline.

Boring bar: a long steel bar with a thread at one end and an adjustable cutter in the middle.

Brail: a rope encircling a boomless mainsail to gather it up to the mast and gaff.

Bridge deck: a deck dividing the companionway from the cockpit.

Bulkhead: a vertical partition separating one part of a vessel from another and adding to the vessel's structural strength.

Bulwarks: the sides of the ship above the deck.

Buoyancy tanks: tanks filled with air or foam, used in lifeboats and dinghies to help to keep the boats afloat should they become waterlogged.

CLR: centre of lateral resistance.

C of E: centre of effort.

Cabin trunk: a low deckhouse.

Capping: bulwark rail.

Carling or carline: structural timbers to which the sides of deckhouses and hatches are fastened, and into which the ends of the half-deck beams are fitted.

Carvel: a method of planking a hull whereby the fore and aft planks fit edge to edge and are fastened to stout frames.

Caulking: the method of filling the seams in deck or topsides with oakum or cotton.

Centreboard: a board or plate which can be lowered through a slot in the keel of a sailing boat to reduce leeway.

Chainplate: a metal strap fastened to the topside of a vessel to which the shrouds are attached.

Cheek pieces: thickening pieces fitted, for instance, on either side of a lifeboat's sternpost, when drilling for a propeller shaft.

Chine: the line where the topside joins the bottom planks of a flat or V-bottomed boat.

Cleat: a two-armed wood or metal deck fitting to which a rope may be belayed.

Clench-fastened: as for Clinker-fastening, but in this case the rooves are omitted, the nails being turned over and hammered flat across the grain of the timber.

Clew: the lower after corner of a fore and aft sail.

Clinker: a method of fastening overlapping planks by driving a copper nail through a bored hole, fitting a roove over the end, cutting the nail short and burring it over the roove with a ball-peen hammer.

Coach screws: heavy, coarse-threaded screws with rectangular heads, sometimes used for holding down an engine to its bearers.

Coble: a high-bowed, flat-sterned NE Coast beach boat.

Cockpit: the well in the stern of a boat from which the vessel is steered.

Companionway: the entry from the deck to the cabin.

Counter: a rounded or square-ended stern that projects aft of the rudder.

Covering board: the outside deck plank which covers the timberheads.

Clamps (or cramps): wrought iron appliances for holding two or more pieces of timber together while they are being glued or fastened.

Cringle: an eye in the bolt rope of a sail.

Cranse iron: a circular iron band through which the bowsprit passes and to which the stays are attached.

Deadwood: a timber bolted on top of the keel, fore or aft, to take the ends of the frames and the lower planks.

Dipping lug: a fore and aft sail bent to a yard and suspended to leeward of the mast. The sail has to be lowered when going about so that the yard and tack of the sail may be brought round the mast when the sail is re-set.

Doghouse: a shelter over a companionway.

Dory: a double-ended, flat-bottomed rowing boat used on the Grand Banks for line fishing.

Drawknife: a tool like a large spokeshave, which is used for stripping spars.

Drop keel: see centreboard.

Electrolysis: chemical decomposition by galvanic action, shown by the effect in seawater of a bronze propeller on the steel hull of a lifeboat. Zinc 'sacrificial' plates are used to take up this action.

Engine bearers: the fore and aft and transverse timbers (which may be floors) for supporting the engine.

Eye-splice: an eye at the end of a rope made up from the strands of the rope, sometimes enclosing a metal thimble.

Fairlead: a wooden or metal deck fitting through which a rope may run.

Fall: the hauling part of a tackle.

Feeler gauge: a gauge for measuring gaps in couplings.

Fender: a cushion of air-filled plastic or rope used to protect the topsides of a vessel when lying alongside a quay or another vessel.

Fiddlehead: a carved scroll on the bows of a vessel, taking the place of a figurehead.

Fife rail: a rail carrying belaying pins, fitted near the mast just above the deck to which the running rigging can be secured.

Fin keel: a fin-shaped keel made up of a steel plate, often with ballast along its lower edge.

Flat-points: wrought iron or mild steel nails used for fastening planks to frames.

Floors: the frames that support and tie the keel.

Foc's'le: the accommodation under the foredeck.

Forepeak: the space up forward below deck.

Frames: the timber (or ribs) to which are fastened the planks.

Freeboard: the amount of the side of a boat above the waterline.

Furl: to fold or gather together a sail.

Gaff: the spar to which the head of a four-sided fore and aft mainsail is bent.

Gaff jaws: the fitting at the inboard end of a gaff, which slides up and down the mast.

Galley: the compartment set aside for cooking and the stowage of cooking vessels in a boat.

Galvanic action: electricity developed by chemical action.

Gammon iron: an iron loop fitting on the stemhead of a boat to hold the bowsprit.

Garboard: the plank next to the keel.

Glues, resin: these are glues that have to be used with a hardening agent. In boatbuilding they have replaced natural glues. Beetle A, Aerolite 300 and Cascophene RS 216M are different brands and types of resin glues.

Gooseneck: the jointed hinged fitting which holds the heel of the boom to the mast.

Gudgeon: a metal eye on the after end of the sternpost to take the rudder pintle.

Gunter: type of rig in which the sail is bent to a yard that is hoisted until it is almost perpendicular. The head of the yard is much higher than the head of the mast.

Gunwale: the timber that extends round the top edge of the topsides of a small craft.

Halyard: the running rigging used for hoisting and lowering sails, flags, yards, etc.

Hambro line: a three-stranded hemp line used for lacings.

Hatch: a covered opening in the deck.

Hawsepipe: the metal pipe through which the anchor cable runs.

Highfield lever: a mechanical device for setting up and letting go a runner.

Hog-piece: a fore and aft timber on top of the keel of a vessel, to which the garboards and frames are fastened.

Hood end: the end of a plank where it fits into the rabbet cut in a stem, transom or sternpost.

Horse: a metal bar across the deck on which travel either the stay-sail or main sheet blocks.

Hounds: wooden shoulders or mast bands at a point on the mast just about the full hoist of a gaff mainsail, to which the shrouds are attached.

Jib: the forward of the two foresails in cutter or other fore and aft rigged vessel.

Keelson: the longitudinal timber (as in ships' lifeboats) which lies on top of the floors and to which the keel is bolted.

Ketch: a two-masted fore and aft rigged sailing vessel with the mizzen mast stepped well ahead of the rudder.

Knees: supports made from natural grown crooks or laminated wood.

Knee, lodging or hanging: lodging knee is a horizontal support for thwarts, deck beams, etc. Hanging knee is a vertical support.

King plank: the centre plank of a foredeck.

LWL: length on waterline.

Leech: the after edge of a fore and aft sail.

Leeboard: wooden or metal plate attached to the sides of a flat bottomed sailing boat which can be lowered to reduce leeway.

Lining (ceiling): planking fastened inside the vessel over the timbers. Fishing boats usually have linings in their holds.

Loose-footed (mainsail): the foot of a sail not laced to a boom.

Luff: the fore edge of a fore and aft sail.

Luff rope: the bolt rope sewn to the fore edge of a fore and aft sail.

Mizzen: the fore and aft sail set on the aft side of the mizzen mast.

Mainsail: the fore and aft sail set on the aft side of the main mast.

Nail-sick: when the fastenings in a hull have corroded and are loose.

Outhaul: the rope and tackle used for hauling a sail out along a spar.

Parrel balls: wooden balls like large beads threaded onto lacings attached to the luff of the main or mizzen sail, to ease the passage of the sail up and down the mast.

Peak: the upper corner of a four-sided sail.

Pin rail: a rail in which belaying pins are fixed.

Pintle: the metal pin on a rudder which slips into the gudgeon on the sternpost to form a hinge.

Punt: a flat-bottomed sailing or rowing boat, also a square-ended river boat.

Quarter installation: the propeller is placed to one side of the sternpost.

Reef: to reduce the sail area by folding and tying, or rolling up, the lower part of the sail.

Reef points: short lengths of line fastened on either side of a sail and used for tying up the reefed part of the sail.

Risings: the inboard strakes (for instance, in a lifeboat), used as supports for the thwarts.

Rooves (or rubs): small round copper washers used in clinker fastening.

Rubbing strake: protective planking to withstand chafe round the top-sides of a vessel.

Runners: adjustable backstays.

Samson post: a single bitt to which the anchor cable can be belayed.

Scandinavian stern: a pointed stern (like a lifeboat's) but with a full rounded deckline and flaring sections aft.

Scarph: to join timbers, beams or planks by halving their ends or cutting them away so that they fit into each other with overlapping.

Scribing: the art of transferring the line of a plank or rabbet to another plank, by the use of a compass or dividers.

Scuppers: openings in a ship's side to allow water to run away.

Shackle: a metal link, usually U-shaped with a bolt screwed across the ends of the arms of the U.

Shaft log: a stout hardwood chock fitted to the inside of the planking to take the stern tube and inner gland bearing.

Sheave: the wheel in the centre of a block or spar over which a rope may run.

Sheerlegs: a primitive derrick made up of two spars crossed at the head with a tackle suspended from this point for lifting heavy weights, stepping masts, etc.

Sheer strake: the uppermost plank of a vessel's topsides.

Sheet: the rope fastened to the clew of the foresail or mainsail.

Shelves: longitudinal timbers to which the ends of the deck beams are fastened.

Shims: thin pieces of metal inserted as spacers and used between the fastening lugs of an engine and its bearers to get correct alignment.

Shrouds: the standing rigging to support a mast athwartships.

Shroud plate: see chainplate.

Sloop: a fore and aft rigged vessel with one headsail.

Spanish windlass: a windlass made by inserting a rod or bolt through a bight of rope and then twisting it to serve as a lever.

Spiling: see Scribing.

Spider bands: iron bands round a mast or spar fitted with eyes to which shrouds or stays or running rigging are attached.

Stay: the standing rigging that runs fore and aft to support the mast.

Staysail: a triangular sail set on a stay. The name usually given to the foresail of a cutter.

Steam box: a contrivance used for steaming planks and timbers, so that they can be bent into shape.

Stem: the foremost timber of the hull of a vessel into which the planks are fitted.

Stern tube: the tube through the stern of a vessel which houses the propeller shaft.

Stockholm tar: a wood tar (as opposed to coal tar) used for the treatment of ropes and also as a preservative for timber.

Stopwater: a plug made of soft wood, driven into a hole bored across a join to make it watertight.

Strake: one of the planks of a vessel's side or bottom.

Stringer: a fore and aft beam or girder.

Strop: a loop of rope or wire fitted round a block or spar.

Tabernacle: the support on deck on which the heel of a mast pivots.

Tack: the lower fore corner of a fore and aft sail.

Talurit: a patent swaged wire splice done under pressure.

Tar varnish: this can range from tar from gasworks to slightly refined bitumastic paint. Useful for steel craft because of its anti-corrosive properties. As a substitute for anti-fouling, a mixture of tar varnish and creosote (80% tar, 20% creosote) is tolerably effective.

Tender: a yacht's dinghy, or any small vessel that serves a larger one.

Throat: the upper fore corner of a fore and aft sail.

Thrust block: the bearings which take the thrust of the propeller.

Thwart: a seat across a dinghy or lifeboat.

Timber-heads: the tops of the frames or timbers.

Timbers: the frames of a vessel.

Topping lift: the rope or ropes used for taking the weight of the boom when raising or lowering sail.

Transom: a type of stern made up of one or more planks athwart the sternpost, to which the ends of the plan are attached.

Traveller: a ring fitting that can be hauled out along a spar or used on a horse to carry a sheet block.

Trowel cement: a filler made up in proprietory forms used to smooth out abrasions or unevenness in a surface that is to be painted.

Tumble-home: the inward inclination of a ship's topsides.

Waterway: a channel for the escape of water.

Web: a triangular piece of metal or wood for joining two girders or frames and beams in a ship.

Windlass: a revolving barrel fitted athwartships in the bows of a smack and used for hauling in the anchor.

Wykeham-Martin: a patent system for furling a jib.

Yard: a spar to which a sail is bent.

Yawl: a fore and aft rigged two-masted vessel whose mizzen mast is set aft of the rudder.

Index